GW00674932

Man of Convictions

Man of Convictions

The life and works of
George Kipper
sinner/songwriter

Edited by Chris Sugden & SID KIPPER

Man of Convictions

Copyright © Chris Sugden 2003

All rights reserved. No part of this publication may be reproduced, stored in a retrieval system, or transmitted, in any form or by any means, electronic, mechanical, photocopying, recording, or otherwise, without the prior consent of the publisher.

First published in 2003 by
Mousehold Press
Victoria Cottage
Constitution Opening
Norwich, NR3 4BD

All songs and tunes in this book are copyright Chris Sugden, or
Dick Nudds and Chris Sugden. We hope you will feel free to sing these songs,
but please be aware that permission is required for any recording,
and fees may be payable. Performance details should be notified
to the Performing Rights Society when requested by them.
Copyright and recording details can be found in the Index.

ISBN 1 874739 26 9

Printed by Barnwells, Aylsham, Norfolk

CONTENTS

AN APPRECIATION OF GEORGE KIPPER by MARTIN CARTHY MBE

In every generation there is one outstanding songwriter. George Kipper's generation consisted of himself and his brother, Henry, so there really wasn't much competition. Nevertheless, Kipper's contribution to English song has been remarkable.

He is probably the most unsung singer-songwriter of our time. Despite many hundreds of compositions, including the incomparable 'Biker Bill', the meretricious 'Illiterate's Alphabet', and the enervating 'Bored Of The Dance', he remains to this day almost totally unrecognised. While this may have something to do with his reputation as a master of disguise, it is nevertheless a situation in need of correction.

Consider his seminal 1985 album 'Live At Her Majesty's Pleasure'. How is it that this record had so little impact compared to another, similar, product? Was it before its time? Was it a capitalist conspiracy? Or was it that Johnny Cash was actually free to leave San Quentain after his recording to promote the album, while Kipper was not in such a fortunate position?

Consider also the appropriation of many of Kipper's rights in his own songs by persons close to this very publication.

George Kipper, while serving a great deal of time, has often been ahead of it. For instance, he was making folk-songs relevant, by bringing them up to date, three decades before the current trend for it began. It is hardly his fault that the world was not then ready for 'Dashing Away With The Soldering Iron'. Or that, when the world finally was ready, the song had become somewhat dated. In fact, many of the songs he made relevant then were so successfully of their time that they are now totally irrelevant once more!

Now, at a time when Norfolk suffers from a severe shortage of old folk-singers, one of the very best languishes in a prison cell. Of course, this does mean that Kipper now has plenty of time for his song-writing. And he has covered the whole gamut: songs to make you think, and songs to stop you thinking; songs to wake you up, and songs to send you into a deep sleep; songs to change the world, and songs to leave it exactly as it was before the song was sung.

It also means, however, that he has been quite unable to protect himself from plagiarism. Some years ago he had high hopes of a song called 'Narborough Fair', but those hopes were dashed by the appearance of another, strangely similar, song. Much the same happened with 'The Streets Of Loddon', and a wonderful ditty about being lost in the dark at sea, called 'Have You Got A Light Buoy?'

George Kipper thoroughly deserves to be up amongst the greats. For far too long he has been down amongst the smalls. And he has surely suffered enough. He has served his time, eaten his porridge, and stuffed his bird. Enough is enough. Except in the case of his songs, of course, in which case enough is rarely sufficient.

So, in closing, I invite you to support the campaign to Free The Trunch One in any way you can. And let he who is without sin cast the first stone. Or she, of course.

M.C.
Robin Hood's Bay, 2003

GEORGE KIPPER

Composting materials collected and sold

No job too small

1934

GEORGE KIPPER and NEPHEW

Menswear, catering and dance-calling

For hands-on service and attention to detail

1962

KIPPER BROTHERS

Scrappers by appointment to the Crown

All metals collected for the war effort

"Give a pot and sink a U-boat"

1940

GEORGE KIPPER ENTERPRIZES
(FOUNDERED 1972)

House Clearances and Reproduction

Furniture our speciality

1973

GEORGE KIPPER ENTERPRIZES

War Surplus and hard to find Commodities

The finest products available brought to your door discreetly

1947

GEORGE KIPPER

DIY   PYO

OK!

M&S   VPL

1980

GEORGE KIPPER ESQ
Holiday Snaps & Portraits

Available next day from the promenade

(Saucy postcards supplied on request)

1951

SID KIPPER

Songs and stories collected and told

No job too big

2003

THE ILLITERATE'S ALPHABET

A is for 'are', like 'are you sixteen?'
Also for 'aural', if you see what I mean;
C's for a 'cue', with which pool is played,
and D is for 'duty', which we try to evade.
　　Honour your teacher and see you do well,
　　Then you'll be certain you know how to spell.

E is for 'eye', it's open, you see,
F is for 'F' - with asterisks, three;
G's for the gnat that gnaws on a gnu,
and H is for 'honest' – would I lie to you?

I's not for Einstein, or eiderdown either,
J is for 'Jasmine', no girl could be blither;
K's for her 'knickers', but not those who take 'em,
and L's for 'Llandudno', if I'm not mistaken.

M's for 'Mnemonics' – with initials so neat,
N's inconclusive, but not incomplete;
O is for 'oestrogen', or so they do tell,
and P's for 'phonetics' which help us to spell.

Q is for 'quay', where boats tie along,
but R's not for writing, unless you've writ wrong;
S is for 'sea', which laps on the shore,
And T's for 'Tsunami', which does rather more.

U's for 'Uranus', it is, I insist,
V's for a 'void', which we all try to miss;
W's for 'why', but also for who,
and X is for 'Xerox', and xylophone too.

Y is for 'you', but, then, so is E,
Z's not for Zar, that's C or it's T;
You'll notice I missed out the one before C;
Well, for present purposes, it's an absolute B!

SID KIPPER SAYS: *"George writ this song recent, when he found out that loads of people in prison can't spell proper. Well, it's not easy. Just take two words – 'champagne', and 'shampoo'. See what I mean? Mind you, when I was a boy that weren't a problem because we didn't have either of them. Back then we had real pain and real poo!"*

GEORGE KIPPER – A MANDATORY LIFE

Kipper's the name. George Kipper. George to my mates. Mister Kipper to you. Maybe it'll be George by the end of the book if you give me a fair hearing and don't bend the corners of the pages over.

I hate page benders. I'd string them up if I had my way. And I'm talking as someone who's been a trusty in the prison library for more than fifteen years. But I'll be coming to that in due course. Before that, I'll begin.

They say I was born on the day World War One finished, and I believe them. November 11th 1918 was a Monday, in case you were wondering. Monday's child is fair of face, they reckon, but that doesn't bother me. I don't have to look at it, do I? Not since I got the beard.

I grew up at Box Cottage. There was my father, Billy, who I always called 'Father', and my mother, Sarah, who I always called 'Sally'. Then she always slapped me on the back of the legs. It was that and the rickets that must have made me a bit bandy. But I wouldn't notice that if I was you. I'm a bit touchy about it. And don't say anything where the words 'passage' and 'pig' come in the same sentence. Even the same paragraph.

Oh yes, I know all about paragraphs. And over the years I've learned a lot about sentences. We did all that stuff at school.

I went to the village school. And then I came home again. Lots of times.

I learned a lot. I learned that whoever invented the 3Rs couldn't spell. I learned it takes one to know one, that one and two makes a crowd, and it takes two to tangle. I didn't learn that it takes four to wife-swap till much later, but I did learn that little girls were different to little boys. And that big girls were something else again. I had what they called an elementary education. Then, when I was fourteen, they chucked me out.

Of course, I was expecting to get chucked out of school. But when I got home that last day to find my bags packed on the doorstep it was quite a shock, I can tell you. Well I am telling you. Father said a few parting words. Through the letter-box. He only had a letter-box for swank. If anyone had ever written to him he couldn't have read it, because he was totally illegitimate. He was a bastard, too.

He told me that it was time for me to make my own way in the world. He said he'd heard there were openings for keen, well-turned-out lads at the Great Hall. I wondered where they were going to find any of them in St Just-near-Trunch. That's my village. It's in Norfolk, if you must know.

It's not a big place. Not even a ham. Just a hamlet, in the north-east corner of the county. In those days it had two pubs, a school, and a few shops. There was a blacksmith, a cobbler, a joiner and a tailor. Now there's just one pub and one shop. So much for progress. But there were plenty of ways then for a young man to make an honest living. If he didn't mind working his way up the hard way. If he didn't mind hard labour, long hours, and low wages.

I minded all of those. Because life was hard enough in those days. Take my elder brother, Henry. Being elder he got taken on as an apprentice in the family business by Father. Seven years he had to work, without earning a penny. I still can't see how it takes seven years to learn road-sweeping.

So I picked up my bags, and I took myself off to the New Goat Inn. Where I got a job straight away as a pot boy. Not a glamorous job. Every seat in that pub was a commode in those days, and someone had to empty them. That someone was me. But all the while I was planning to move on to bigger things. And I don't mean a job as a nightsoil man. You hear things in a pub. In my job I smelt things too, but it was what I heard that interested me. What's what. Who's who. Where's when. That sort of thing. And it wasn't long before I persuaded them to take me along on a night's poaching.

THE LAY OF THE LASS

As he roved out one November morning,
All searching for a lay;
A maid he heard who sang these words;
"Who'll whack my diddle, the day?"

So boldly now he stepped up to her,
Without a how-d'you do;
Saying, "Now, sweet Miss, if you'll assist,
I'll whack your diddle, for you."

"Stand off," she said,"For your intention
Is but to bushwack me;
For you would score my precious store,
And leave me here to grieve."

Oh, but when she saw his propelling pencil,
Her eyes they opened wide.
Then did she say: "Sir, you must have your way;
Come, whack my diddle," she cried.

So he took down her dainty crotchets,
Put his finger in her ear;
Then very neat, all on a sheet,
Her parts he entered there.

He had her then between two covers;
Till she gave him her all.
With pencil finished, and no lead in it,
He'd whacked her diddle, withal.

So come all young maids that meet a rover,
Don't let your bush be whacked.
When in the field keep your lips sealed,
And hold your diddle intact!

SID KIPPER SAYS: *"Some people think folk-songs are full of nonsense, what with all their fol-de-rols and fiddle-me-dees. They don't know what they're missing. Take this one. It's what they call a half-entendre. It sounds filthy, but it's actually about collecting folk-songs. No nonsense there."*

They didn't call it poaching, of course. They called it 'putching'. Because they were good old Norfolk boys, and they didn't know any worse. So I helped them with their 'putching'. And they thanked me kindly, and I left empty-handed. Another lesson learned. But not the one you might think. Because we all got stopped by the keepers on the way home, and they couldn't pin anything on me. So they all got three months, and all I got was "We'll be keeping an eye on you, young Kipper-me-lad." That and a clip round the ear. But that was standard practice in them days. You expected it. If you'd met a keeper and came away with your ear unclipped, well, you'd feel diminished. Times were hard, but we were harder.

I soon learned that the most successful poachers weren't the one's who knew the ways of the wood and the habits of the wildlife. They were the ones who knew the ways of the keepers and the habits of the police. That other stuff is all very well, but a bird in the bush is worth two in the hand when the constabulary want to know what you've been up to. Never mind what you've read in *Tooth And Claw*. *The Police Gazette* is a lot more use.

I hadn't been working at the Goat long when I got my first business break. This bloke came in who'd got an unexpected surplus of bicycle clips. He was prepared to part with them for the right price. No questions asked. So I gave him an answer. He gave me a higher one back, and we met in the middle. With a tanner back for luck.

What he didn't know was I'd heard something. I'd heard some of them talking about going ratting. Now I was about to introduce them to something. It was the brand new, up-to-the-minute replacement for tying a bit of string round your ankles. I doubled my money overnight. That money went to the printers. For labels. 'Kipper's Patent Compost Starter', they said. '100-per-cent natural ingredients'. Well, I could vouch for that. I collected those ingredients in the Goat every night. Very fresh they were, too.

When I tell youngsters that, they think I'm taking the pee. But I wasn't just taking it, was I? I was taking it, and then selling it on at a profit.

That got me started in business. But it was just the start. Later I sold that business on to Claude Cockle. Of course, when they did the pub up he had to bribe the plumbers. Otherwise he'd have lost his raw material. And let's face it, you can't get much rawer than sewage.

There's another thing I used to hear in the pub. Singing. Proper singing, I mean. What nowadays they call folk-singing. And there was money in that, too. In fact, it's been a steady earner for me all my life, one way and another.

Back then it was the folk-song collectors. Now, I had to be a bit careful with them. Because my family had loads of folk-songs, but Father was very strict about not giving them to collectors. Something to do with not wanting to have his dirty bits cut out. But there were songs that had fallen into disuse. Songs that nobody wanted any more. And as long as I handed them over discreetly, round the back, there was no harm done. Of course, a lot of those old boys were happy to give away their songs just for a few drinks. But I've always reckoned that cash is the sincerest form of flattery.

HADDISCOE MAYPOLE SONG

Come las-ses and lad-dies, take leave of your dad-dies, For May-day is come, you know; Come

lad-dies and wen-ches, take leave of your sen-ses, Aw-ay to the May-pole go. Now

Ga-ry will go with Gail, and Lar-ry will go with Lill; Har-ry will go with

Hil-lar-y Hake, and Bar-ry will go with Bill. Sing-ing Had-dis-coe, thun-der rum-ble

oh, The wind is up, the sun it hides aw-ay-ay oh; We must dance the

sum-mer in, all in the pour-ing rai-ain oh; For sum-mer is a com-ing in, at

least they say it may oh!

SID KIPPER SAYS: *"Until George got hold of it there was only a bit of the original song. Then he done a proper restoration job on it, like he used to do with old furniture. It's just a matter of replacing missing bits, doing some filling, and then adding the wear marks. Only an expert could tell it from the real thing."*

I unloaded a fair few songs that nobody round our way wanted any more. Stuff like the Haddiscoe Maypole Song. I often wonder what came of some of those old songs. I used to wonder what the collectors wanted them for. Well, I found out soon enough. Before long we had people coming into the Goat with these books they'd bought. And in them were all these old songs. But there were gaps where the dirty bits used to be. And these people wanted to collect the dirty bits to stick them in their books. Well, I could help there. And if I didn't know the exact actual dirty bits for that particular song I could soon get some. How were they to know the dirty bits I sold them came from another song? And if they did notice, that only made them all the more excited. Then they reckoned they'd discovered something. A variant. And those variants, it seemed, were worth even more. Which set me to thinking. If what they wanted was songs that were different to the right ones, well, who was I to deny them?

Come lasses and laddies, take leave of your daddies,
For Mayday is come, you know;
Come laddies and wenches, take leave of your senses,
Away to the Maypole go.
Now Gary will go with Gail, and Larry will go with Lill;
Harry will go with Hillary Hake, and Barry will go with Bill.
Singing Haddiscoe, thunder rumble-oh,
The wind is up, the sun it hides away-oh;
We must dance the summer in, all in the pouring rain-oh;
For summer is a-coming in, at least they say it may-oh.

Now is your chance to join in the dance,
So take your lover in hand,
For April has gone, but May is come,
And here she sweetly stands.
Now take her in your arms, and if your cards you play,
With any luck you'll later pluck the darling buds of May.

With your May queen you must go to the green,
To make some mayhem there;
And dance, mayhap, while thunder claps,
And lightning rends the air.
With ribbons gleaming wet, and shining iron pole,
Full soon you will feel such a thrill to banish all the cold.

Now our little band is the best in the land,
With drums and pipes, and so
The girls and boys make a wonderful noise,
As they eagerly bang and blow.
Though downpour turn to flood, they never will dismay;
And you'll hear their cries as the water's rise, "Mayday! Mayday! Mayday!"

Jump higher and higher until you all tire,
And then jump higher still.
For every Willie shall have his Win,
And every Fanny her Phil.
And though the wind may howl, keep one thought in your head;
You'll get a kiss, on your chilblained lips, before you go to bed.

Since Adam and Eve every Sally and Steve
Have risen to dance in the May.
So though you moan, and grump and groan,
You're dancing anyway.
Now jump and jig a jig, although the day be drear,
And then you'll say, at the end of the day, thank God that's all over this year.

THE BANKER'S DAUGHTER

A banker's fair daughter I once did befriend,
She asked if my assets to her I would lend?
"I'm Penny," she said, as her locks I admired;
"I could get you a loan if that's what you required."

I explained that I needed a place that was right,
To put in my treasure and keep it there tight.
Penny said, "You value your goods, I can see;
And I'll nurture them well if you'll give them to me."

"If you come with me, sir, I'm sure I'm not wrong,
I'll show you the place where your booty belongs."
She seemed quite alarmed when I entered her closet,
But her interest rose when I made my deposit.

Before very long our transaction was done;
She said, "To mix business with pleasure's my fun."
"Likewise," I replied, "I cannot tell you how,
But I'd like to withdraw a little something for now."

I was sure such a girl would be fully insured,
But in nine months came word that my nest egg had matured.
My holdings had outcomes I could not evade;
My interest had fallen, but the fees must be paid.

Her father insisted that he would not barter;
He wouldn't be happy till I was a partner.
So look after your pounds, if you would have great wealth,
For Penny, be sure, will look after herself.

SID KIPPER SAYS: *"You get loads of these songs where young men rove out and meet willing young maidens. Well I've roved out loads of times, and it's never happened to me. I reckon I must be roving wrong."*

8

So I used to sit in my little room, over the snug bar, thinking of dirty bits. I found it helped if I thought of Ruby. She was the Buxton barmaid. I came up with a lot of stuff that way. You'd be surprised how many dirty bits a sixteen year old with time on his hands can come up with. The Cuckoos Nest. That was one of mine. The Banker's Daughter was another. It was easy. A few lines. A couple of repeats. Some fol-de-rols. And Charlie's your aunt! Put in a few Ĕds, like 'walkÈd' and 'talkÈd', and those collectors couldn't tell the difference.

I learned quick. I found that the more dirty bits a song had, the better they liked it. That meant they could leave bigger gaps in their books. It saved on the ink. And that meant the people who bought the books had more to fill in. And there I was, only too willing to help them. For a consideration.

In a couple of years I'd built up quite a pile of considerations. I kept it under the mattress. It got hard to sleep. Well most of those considerations were in coin.

Now, I'd heard of banks. But none of our family had ever had anything to do with them. It was nothing personal. It was just that we had nothing they wanted. And they weren't about to give us anything we wanted. But I managed to get my considerations into a wheelbarrow without anyone knowing. And I set off and walked it to Gurnards Bank. That's in North Walsham.

I had a hell of a job getting the barrow up all those steps and through the revolving doors. But I did it. And then they had the cheek to look down their noses at me. Someone said something about the tradesmen's entrance being round the back. Well, I soon changed that. Because money talks. And mine said, "Look, here's this young no-nothing with loads of cash." But they were still suspicious. They wanted to know who I was. Well, I knew that. They wanted to know where I'd got the money from. I knew that too. They asked me lots of questions, but in the end they took the money and put it in their safe. I got a bank book, and that was that.

Shame I never thought to ask them any questions. Along the lines of, "Are you going to get robbed tonight?"

I read about it a fortnight later. In the *North Norfolk News and Agitator*. In the pub I only heard very local stuff.

So, next chance I got I went to North Walsham to ask the score. According to the bank it was nil–nil. They hadn't got my money, and neither had I. They reckoned it was all in the small print. They said my money had to be in the bank for five working days before it was there officially. I'd seen how they worked. At that pace five working days would take them a month. So where was my money in the meantime, I asked. Oh, they said. It was actually in the safe. It just wasn't officially in the safe. Until the five days were up it was still my responsibility. And to be frank, they said, I'd been pretty irresponsible with it, hadn't I?

I could have shouted. I could have got violent. I could have refused to leave. But I know when I've been done up. I'm a Kipper, after all. So I kept my cool. I turned round and walked out of the bank. And I swore an oath that I'd never go into a bank ever again.

And if I'd stuck to that oath I wouldn't be where I am now.

THE WIGHTON WALNUT SONG

Come all you gloom-y fel-lows, and list-en to my song, For
un-like Crom-er mag-ist-rates I won't de-tain you long. It's of a bold young
nut-ter, who lived ar-round this way; Went out one sun-ny morn-ing, for to
get his nuts in May. With me ran-tan-tan and me rin-tin-tin, with a
woah! and a way-hay - hay; And when she saw his nuts so trim she could not him gain-
- say.

I was back at the bottom of life's snake again. Well, I'd just have to find another ladder. By now the folk-song collecting craze was on the wane. The compost starter business was steady. And unless Ernie improved his beer it would stay that way. Then there was the singing. Perhaps I could make more of that. What I wanted was a gimmick. A dodge.

Which was how I came to the walnuts. They'd belonged to my grandfather, Daniel Kipper. Known in the village as 'Doornail'. Because he was dead.

The walnuts had been handed down to Aunt Maud, and when she died in 1933 they'd come to me. Walnut-shells to be precise. A top-of-the-range set, in a hand-tooled nut-case. You've probably seen them played by my nephew Sid. He's not bad. But I've forgotten more than I ever knew about the walnut-shells. Because I was the one who revived them. No one had played them for years.

I practised in my little room, over the snug bar. I took to the walnut-shells straight off. What you have is two walnuts, split in halves. You strap them to your fingers. Then you bang them together. 'Concussion instruments' Sid calls them. They've got a long history. I'll get him to put in a bit about that.

I got quite good. I could play all the moves. The Walnut Whirl. The Nutmeg. The Wheel Nut. They're very physical, the walnut-shells. I really needed a bigger room. Then I had to learn to sing at the same time, which meant finding a suitable song. I tried 'The Lark In Mourning'. It wasn't right. I tried 'I Gave My Love A Fever'. That wasn't right, either. I just couldn't find the right old song. So I made up a new old song. My first big hit. 'The Wighton Walnut Song'.

Come all you gloomy fellows, and listen to my song,
For unlike Cromer magistrates I won't detain you long.
It's of a bold young nutter, who lived around this way;
Went out one sunny morning, for to get his nuts in May.
    With me ran-tan-tan and me rin-tin-tin, with a woah! and a way-hay-hay;
    And when she saw his nuts so trim she could not him gainsay.

It's of young May the milkmaid, a-walking in the wood,
A-minding her own bus-i-ness, just as a milk-i-maid should;
A-minding her own bus-i-ness, amidst the bushes, but
She could not help but notice when he played upon his nuts.

She watched the way he handled his nuts so neat and clever,
It made her eyes to water when he banged them both together.
She said, "Kind sir, your music I never will forget,
But if you've no objection, then we'll make this a duet."

She loosened all her petticoats, for exercise she planned;
She set her feet akimbo and she took his nuts in hand.
She said, "Now you are shy, sir, I see that very well,
But I have a little nut bush that will draw you from your shell."

Now Ted and May are married and have nutkins of their own,
But still they make their music, when they get some time alone.
He'll bid her set the tempo, and smiling she will say:
"If you will wield the baton, sir, you'll have your nuts in May."

SID KIPPER SAYS: *"Walnuts was first brought into the country by the Romans, who smuggled them in through Customs. Nobody knows when they were first brought into the city. I don't know why the Romans bothered, because nobody was playing the walnuts then, so it was a waste of time. Of course, when they did start playing them they came in very handy, so that was a bit of luck really.*

The next important thing in a brief history was the invention of knicker elastic. Of course this was important for other things beside walnut-shells. It was important for knickers, for a start, because before that they were falling down all the time. No wonder they call them the good old days! Anyhow, before this the walnut-shells were tied on with ribbons. You couldn't do that yourself, so each player had to have a ribbontieroner to tie their ribbons on. When elastic was invented the ribbontieroners went on strike in protest, but that was a waste of time as they'd all just been sacked. Their descendants are still on strike as a matter of fact. They have an annual demo when they march around Trunch in their bath chairs, cut any knicker elastic they can get their hands on, and then settle down to talk about the good old days round a burning brassière. But the ribbons never came back, except for ceremonial occasions.

Playing the walnuts died out totally around the turn of the last century, until it got taken up again by my Uncle George. He was the first of the modern players, if you can call someone modern who reckons that mobile phones will never catch on because there's no cord to play with. Finally, I started playing the shells, and their place in history was assured, because they were being played by such a famous megostar.

Warning – this song may contain nuts!"

THE CRUEL SHE

Last Christmas my wife said to me, all forlorn,
Her dress was all frayed, and her coat was all torn;
I'm eager to please, but she called me mean,
When I gave her a second-hand sewing machine!
    Oh, you can't please a woman, whatever you say;
    Never mind, for she'll please herself, anyway!

When her birthday approached, my wife had a grouse,
She said I should get her some help round the house,
I'm eager to please, but she threw quite a strop,
When I gave her a smart, matching bucket and mop.

On our anniversary she said I didn't care:
The proof was I never took her anywhere.
I'm eager to please, drove her to a hotel,
But she thought that I should have stayed there as well.

This Christmas I simply asked what she desired.
Something lacy and white would be right, it transpired.
I'm eager to please, so I bought a string vest;
And it's really too painful to tell you the rest.

So I left my wife, and found me another,
She was easy to please, and kind as a mother.
She gave me something which caused me to swoon;
I do hope they find a cure for it soon!
    No, you can't please a woman, but, if you could,
    You couldn't then claim to be misunderstood!

SID KIPPER SAYS: *"Buying presents for women can lead to trouble. Buy one of them something not intimate enough and you're in trouble. Buy another one something too intimate and you're in even more trouble. Especially from the first one."*

'The Wighton Walnut Song' got me noticed. It got me invited to go to other pubs to sing. Sometimes by the people in the other pubs. What's more, all those pubs had commodes. So business began to boom.

But the biggest thing was the walnut-shells. People heard about them and wanted to see them. When they had, they wanted to see them again. In case they'd been seeing things the first time. At first I used to take a collection. Other than the commode one. I soon had more washers than Aylsham Laundry. So I started charging the landlords. Except where they were landladies. I had a different arrangement with them.

Until I discovered something. A man who shows he can handle his nuts can have his pick of women. It must be what they call 'pathetic magic'. Nuts being – well, you know. And banging being – well, you know that too. Then there's all the suggestive movements. Suffice it to say, the walnuts are the best way I've ever found to get to – well, the kernel of the matter. What they call round Thetford 'the sweet wrinkled walnut'. And if you don't know what that is I can't tell you in mixed company.

But I'm telling you too much anyway. Too much detail. None of your business, really. So I'll stick to the important things in my history. Like my brother, Henry, getting married. To Agnes Spratt. Known to everyone as 'Dot'. They married, and she went to Gorleston on honeymoon. So did I. Henry stayed at home to look after his ferrets. I looked after Dot. Had a marvellous time. Time flies when you're enjoying someone.

I liked married life so much that when I got back I made a proposal to Ruby Cube, the Buxton barmaid. She was having none of it. Oh, she wanted some of it. But only if I married her. So I did.

It was a marvellous wedding. St Just's church looked fantastic in the June sunshine. The churchyard was bursting with flowers. Perhaps we should have got married there. As it was we went to the Registry Office in North Walsham and made it legal. That went against the grain, I must admit. I mean, I don't mind being legal as such. It's just that it seemed a bit much to go out of the way for it. Then we had five harmonious days in the Isle of Wight. As we left I thought I'd always think of it as a happy place. I wondered if I'd ever come back. Little did I know.

We settled down in a cottage on Jimmy Hill. Ruby kept on as a barmaid. I kept on as a customer. I had my irons in several fires. Singing. Compost. Bird wringing. That's where you wring a bird's neck so you can tell where it goes. It goes in the shed. Until you can find a customer.

So it was all going quite nicely when war broke out. There I was. I was twenty years old. I was fit and healthy. I knew how to shoot a gun. So it was urgent I got myself into a reserved occupation straight away. Otherwise I'd be called up.

Now I won't have it said that my family are conscientious objectors. We're not. We're not conscientious at all. We're just objectors. Plain and simple. We object to having to leave home. To doing what other people order us to. Most of all we object to being shot at. But folk-singing wasn't reserved. I don't know why not. Somebody's got to do it, after all. Nor was composting. Not even bird wringing. So I asked about, and quickly set up a scrapping business with my brother Henry. Scrapping was reserved. Because in the war people went mad for scrapping. They scrapped their pots, and their pans, and their iron railings. So we used to collect them, and take them over to the depot in Aylsham. We reckoned we were doing our bit. Well, I was certainly doing my bit. And, I confess, one or two other people's bits. But I won't go into that just now.

THE TROUSERS IN BETWEEN

Now a chap must keep in shape if he's going to cut a dash, And I'm a real dash-cut-ter, you can tell. You have to watch your weight if you're go-ing to be flash, Oh a swell just can-not af-ford to swell. But some parts of a per-son are not eas-il-il-y seen; The parts a per-son per-ches on, if you see what I mean. But with a pair of look-ing glas-ses, you could see just where your arse is, If it was-n't for the trous-ers in bet-ween.

SID KIPPER SAYS: *"This was an old musical-hall song what was recorded years ago by my Uncle Jimmy. George took the first verse, then wrote three new ones. So now it's neither one thing nor the other. And everyone knows that one thing is one thing, but the other is something else."*

I sort of got to like the idea of going round, getting something for nothing. I'm talking about the scrap again now. Then one day the bloke at the depot told me something shocking. Though not before he made me sign the Unofficial Secrets Act. Then he told me they didn't really want the scrap at all. It was only being collected for morale. To make people feel they were doing their bit. Well, that set me to thinking. If it was good for people to give the stuff, but nobody really wanted it, there was a market in the gap. And why stop at brass and iron and copper? What about silver and gold? Surely people giving those away would feel even better about the war effort. And as the depot didn't really want them, it was my patriotic duty to help out. And while I was helping out I might as well help myself.

Well, you get my drift. Suffice it to say that by the end of the war St Just was one of the moralist places in the country, without a scrap of metal to be seen in the place. As to where it all went, well, that's for me to know and you to mind your own business.

But some other stuff happened before then. For a start, in 1941, Jimmy, my second-cousin several times removed, died. Well, it wasn't exactly a start for him. Or, if it was, I don't know what it was the start of. Mind you, he'd died loads of time before. If not so finally.

Now a chap must keep in shape if he's going to cut a dash,
And I'm a real dash-cutter, you can tell.
You have to watch your weight if you're going to be flash,
Oh a swell just cannot afford to swell.
But some parts of a person are not easilily seen;
The parts a person perches on, if you see what I mean.
But with a pair of looking glasses, you could see just where your arse is,
If it wasn't for the trousers in between.

Now on the sporting field I'm a wonder to behold,
I can run, and jump, and throw, and put the shot.
I really look the part, or so I have been told,
Though I never have been told the part of what.
I like to look my smartest when I'm playing at the sport,
And I get admiring glances from my athletic support,
But when I do the high jump you could tell I'm wearing Y-fronts,
If it wasn't for the trousers in between.

Now when it comes to dancing I cannot tell you false,
I really am as good as any pro.
I can foxtrot, I can polka, I can minuet and waltz,
And the ladies all admire my fandango.
Mrs Fawcett wondered what I'd look like in ballet,
In tights and pumps and tunic, well, I can only say
That when we did the lancers, she'd have found out all the answers
If it wasn't for the trousers in between.

Now when you mix with Viscounts, and Countesses and Earls,
You have to watch your Ps and Qs and Zs.
A large vocabulary impresses all the girls,
And a well-turned phrase can really turn their heads.
So if you do not wish to ever sound absurd,
Learn the dictionary, and the order of the words.
For the trousseau of the strumpet would be up against the trumpet,
If it wasn't for the trousers in between.

He used to be on the Music Halls, years before. He'd done almost everything there. None of it successfully. Which was probably why he was removed so many times. He was a singer, a comic, a juggler. All them. But never a good one of any of them. He did have a bit of fame when he joined up with three other fellows. They appeared at the Hall in Aylsham, dressed up in horned hats, and calling themselves 'The Four Norsemen Of The Acropolis'. People said at least it was better than his normal act. They reckoned the jokes were funnier in Norse.

For a while he was what they called a stand-up comic. That meant that when he told a joke the audience used to stand up and walk out.

Of course he still got work while the old Trunch Empire was open, because he knew the management. In fact he brought the house down. Well, not exactly. It was just that nobody told him they were beginning the demolition. But he survived that. In fact they erected a plaque on the very spot where he'd been standing. It said, 'The Management accepts no responsibility for anything whatsoever'. I used it as a basis for contracts for years.

Jimmy never actually retired. Later in life he tried to drink himself stupid, but it was too late for that. So he was still touring Womens Institutes and failing to entertain the troops right up to the end. If you ask me it was the boos that finished him.

DOWN, DUVET, DOWN

A young man come courting me, hey down, duvet down;
Wanted to marry me, he being young.
He loved me for myself, despite my enormous wealth,
    Maids when you're old always wed a young man!
    He's got loads of fallurum, fie-liddle-eye-uram,
    So maids when you're old always wed a young man.

On the morn of our marriage vows, high down, duvet down;
He came round to my house, he being young.
He ran upstairs, God bless, to help my young niece get dressed,

When we got to the church, hold down, duvet down;
For my sister he did search, he being young.
He kindly spent an hour, showing her round the tower,

We went to the wedding feast, hoe down, duvet down;
His kindness never ceased, he being young.
In the back room he thanked my bridesmaid personally,

When all the guests had gone, hic down, duvet down;
Once more his breeding shone, he being young.
He gave me some time alone, while he walked my best friend home,

When he came to bed I thought, hard down, duvet down;
He'd be too tired for sport, he being young.
But he shouted 'fore!' and blast, I opened my score, at last,

When he went to sleep, hang down, duvet down;
Out of bed I did creep, he being young.
I left him there alone, 'cos there were two more like him at home,

Another thing that happened in 1941 was I began to do deliveries. Well, I was already collecting, wasn't I? I started by selling pots and pans. I had loads of them, after all. And it gave people a change to be patriotic, by giving them back to me. It was a perfect business. A guilt-edged certainty. Just as long as you remembered who'd already had which pots. Then one or two asked if I could get them things off the ration. And I always thought I had an honest face! Well, as it happened I could lay my hands on certain things. Pheasants, rabbits, stuff like that. Then I made a few contacts at the depot, and before long I had another nice little earner. Strictly speaking it was against the law. But not what you'd really call illegal.

But Henry didn't like it. He kept going on about it interfering with the war effort. I said if the war effort was up to him we'd already have lost. And anyway, rabbits ate crops, didn't they? Then he said in that case he ought to get a cut. So I told him I wouldn't dream of causing him suffering by being part of what he didn't approve of. It turned into quite a row. We didn't speak for years, which suited me. He hadn't got anything I wanted to hear. We still worked together.

And then, in 1942, I found out what it caused. Because that was the year my boy Len was born.

Being a father meant a lot of changes. Mostly of nappies. Well, Ruby kept on the barmaid job, so I was left holding the baby most nights. There's not a lot to this women's work if you ask me. The only thing I couldn't do with my hands tied behind my back was the feeding. You have to have a woman for that. So at feeding time I had to take him down to the Goat. Some fathers don't take their sons for a drink together at the pub till they're eighteen. Well I took mine when he was just six weeks! We used to get in the snug bar, and Ruby used to supply us both. Although I usually had mine in a mug.

And Ruby never minded the spectators. She said it cost her nothing, so if it gave them pleasure that was a bonus, wasn't it. Not like my brother Henry. He said that a pleasure shared is a pleasure halved. But I wasn't listening. And it didn't keep him out of the snug at feeding time.

Some people say I like a drink. Well, let's stamp that out straightaway. I hate a drink. That's just tantalising. I like lots of drinks. But I was always careful when I was with the child. Until he learned to crawl, anyway. Then we sometimes used to crawl home together. Mind, we had to be careful not to get caught by PC Clam being drunk and disorderly. But that wasn't any real problem. He was always in the public bar, keeping a blind eye on things. I used to send him drinks through. That meant he was too busy to worry about me. And if I went out for a little nature watching after Ruby got home, well, he'd be in no state. Anyhow, there was a war on, so he wasn't allowed to show a light. That was another thing in my favour.

But I mustn't give the wrong impression. I wasn't faithful to Ruby, or anything like that. Well, it's not natural, is it? I mean, if God had meant us to be faithful to our wives he wouldn't have given us other people's wives. Anyhow, we got registered at the office. So it was none of His business. I saw the Registrar occasionally, and he never said anything about it. And I was very discreet. I always made sure the coast was clear. And used the side entrance. Even at home.

THE BOLD LOW WAY MAN

Oh I once was Bold True-man, but now I've been caught; I've had thous-ands of rich-es, but I'll leave here with nought. And my neck it will pay for the life that I've led, Which is ve-ry bad news for my bo-dy and head! Cry-ing stand and de-liv-er; stand and de-liv-er; I held up Lord Prior till my arms grew quite tired, Cry-ing stand and de-liv-er.

SID KIPPER SAYS: *"When you sing the first line of this song in Yorkshire they think it's about cricket. Well, it isn't."*

Oh I once was Bold Trueman, but now I've been caught;
I've had thousands of riches, but I'll leave here with nought.
And my neck it must pay for the life that I've led,
Which is very bad news for my body and head!
Crying stand and deliver; stand and deliver;
I held up Lord Prior till my arms grew quite tired,
Crying stand and deliver.

My father had nothing; my mother had less.
She was big, blonde and busty – but there I digress,
For when I was born she'd not even a bed,
So she stood and delivered, and I fell on my head.
She had to stand and deliver; stand and deliver;
But what made it unfair was she stood on a chair,
To stand and deliver.

My sweetheart was Bess, and the truth I must tell,
Oh I loved her often, and she loved me well;
But with her, at the altar, I was captured almost,
For she'd put an announcement in the *North Norfolk Post*!
I couldn't stand and deliver; stand and deliver;
I fled through the mist, as the guests all got kissed;
I couldn't stand and deliver.

18

Of course, the baby-sitting did interfere with the singing. The hours conflicted. I tried singing lullabies to the child, but he always bust out screaming. I never knew whether he was objecting or joining in. I kept my hand in with the walnut-shells, though. He liked them. They made him chortle. They still do, as a matter of fact. Or they did last time I had the chance. Where I am at the moment they're not allowed. Something to do with cruel and inhuman treatment, they reckon.

One of the warders just came round. I don't know who knocked him out. I gave him some water and a sit down on my bunk. He was moaning about his pension. He reckoned it was getting worth less and less. My nephew Sid could have told him. 'A penny saved is a penny halved.' That's one of Sid's favourites. That reminded me of the Christmas club we used to have in the village. It was sort of traditional. What happened was that every week people used to hand a bit of money to this bloke. That kept on through the year. Then, just before Christmas, the bloke who took the money disappeared and was never seen again. I thought of setting one up myself at one time, but I wasn't that ambitious to travel.

As for the scrapping, I had it all to myself. Henry got injured when I dropped a tin bath on him. I had to visit him in hospital. I didn't talk to him, obviously, because we still weren't speaking. But according to the nurse he had a serious complaint, and was in a critical condition. Turned out he was complaining about the food, and being critical of the decor. I told her not to worry. He was always like that. He was something chronic. Eventually he got invalided out of the scrapping, and went on the sick. Which was where he stayed until 1984.

But I'm getting previous again. In 1944 I had my first serious brush with the law.

> I robbed from the rich and I gave to the poor,
> Till after a while they weren't poor any more.
> So I robbed back from them all that ill-gotten wealth;
> And decided 'twas fairer to keep it myself.
> Singing stand and deliver; stand and deliver;
> Anyway they're so thick that they'd just have it nicked,
> Singing stand and deliver.
>
> I've swiped and I've swindled, I've nobbled and nicked;
> Sneaked, snatched and snaffled, and played dirty tricks.
> I've purloined and pilfered and pillaged and lynched,
> And I once told a fib to a nun in Easy Wynch.
> Crying stand and deliver; stand and deliver;
> Oh what times I have had; it's so good to be bad,
> Crying stand and deliver.
>
> I was grabbed by the Peelers, which caused me to shout,
> And then at my trial all my misdeeds came out.
> The judge he looked stern as he donned the black cap,
> With white gloves and red tights, plus a nice fur-trimmed wrap.
> He said stand and deliver; stand and deliver;
> So I begged for my life, while he eyed up my wife,
> He said stand and deliver.
>
> But the judge didn't heed me – his hearing was hardened –
> And when I asked, "What's the sentence?", his answer was "Pardon?"
> So they had to free me despite my transgression,
> Therefore please disregard all the previous confession.
> It's back to stand and deliver; stand and deliver;
> You'll see no repentance, I've got a very short sentence,
> Which is "Stand and deliver."

THE KNAPTON WHITE HARE

In the fields around Knapton, so I have heard tell,
There in the stubble a white hare did dwell;
And we had decided that white hare to try;
Whether innocent or guilty we'd know by and by.

So me and Anne Chovey began and did start,
But we hadn't a greyhound that white hair to hunt,
We hadn't a greyhound, 'twas all our complaint
But we had a red setter and a pot of grey paint.

So it's up with the brush, and the job was soon done
And it's over to Knapton we straightway have gone;
So straight and so true, like some arrow in flight,
But unlike an arrow, at Trunch we turned right.

When we got to Knapton the hare was soon found;
Though the paint was still wet, we let loose the hound;
The setter took off with the hare close behind,
Well, that wasn't exactly what we had in mind.

And then in a moment that dog it did point;
Well the paint it had set, and it froze every joint.
That setter was solid from toe unto top,
But coming up behind it, the hare couldn't stop.

That white hare turned pale – I swear that it's true –
As straight for that rigid dog's tail it flew:
The hare was proved guilty, and justice prevailed;
It died at the end of a shaggy dog's tail.

Well our case it came up and our trial it was held,
And me and Ann Chovey got a month in the cells;
The dog was transported – 'twas grossly unfair;
Seven years in Australia for just splitting hares.

SID KIPPER SAYS: *"This song should be sung so as to tell the story. Some people would say loosely, but I say not too loosely. Not above six or seven pints loose. Otherwise you'd be so loose you'd be tight, and then no one would be able to understand what you were on about. Although in that case I suppose it wouldn't matter how you sang it."*

You'd think they'd have better things to do, what with the war. Anyhow, officially my nose was clean. I had a note from the doctor to say so. And they'd tried it before. The first time was when I was only twelve. Some trumped-up charge like 'Possession of bread with intent to supply'. Well, I was a part-time delivery boy for the bakery, after all. Anyhow, possession is nine parts of the law, isn't it? Nothing had come of it.

But now Clam decided he was going to get me. I think Lord Silver-Darling was getting on to him about the amount of game he was losing. But Clam could hardly creep up on me. He was six foot two, and the same round. He didn't really need a bike. He could roll from place to place. And he didn't like me calling him 'Clammy', either.

So one day I noticed he was following me. Wherever I went, whatever I did, all that day he was there. Which was a bit inconvenient. It meant I couldn't get on with things that needed doing. But I put up with it until he finally followed me home from the Goat. And that, I thought, was the end of it.

Imagine my shock, then, when the next day I was summonsed to the police station. In North Walsham. They took my fingerprints, photographed me, and charged me with 'Wasting Police Time'. I told them I'd done nothing wrong. They said that was the trouble. They said Clam had followed me all day, and as I'd done nothing wrong then I was wasting his time. It had me worried at first. But I soon realised it was just a try-on. A warning. What my Uncle Albert used to call 'a shit across the bows'. So it was just a matter of sitting out the day in the cells, until they threw me out and left me to walk home.

They also accused me of telling stories. Well, that was fair enough. All those evenings at home with the baby, I'd developed quite a repertoire. Jack And The Beans Talk. Aladdin And His Amazing Lump. But it wasn't just children's stories. Not by any mean of manners. I could do grown-up stories as well. Our family has always been known for telling tales. Uncle Albert could regale you for hours. Whether you liked it or not. He had all sorts of stories. About mermaids, and ghost ships. Cruel captains, and fresh-cheeked cabin boys bursting out of their waistcoats. Far off lands, and exotic climbs. Although whether he really was the first man to the top of Everest I can't say. But I can guess.

Albert had an endless selection of stories. Not like my brother Henry. He had a collection of endless stories. That was because he was so boring he used to send himself to sleep. Before he'd got half-way through.

Some people think story-telling is easy. Well, they're right. But story-telling that people actually want to hear, that's more difficult. You need talent. I suppose that's why I was so good at it. Come to think of it. I suppose that's why Sid's so good as well. And he's taken it a lot further. He's got hundreds of stories. Like 'The Shaming Of The True'. And that one about the opera singer marooned on a desert island. 'The Romance Of Robinson Caruso'. And people actually want to hear Sid's stories. It's the way he tells them. He's even done some of them in books, and on albums. Of course, when I was young, albums were books. Now they're compacted disks and the like. Which is all very well. But then you need a compacted disk player, and speakers and everything. You don't need all that with a book.

Compacted disks do have one advantage over books. You can't bend the corners of a compacted disk. Because it hasn't got any.

21

THE OUTRAGEOUS NIGHT

Next door's dog is always yapping, all through the night;
Just when decent folk are napping, all through the night;
Though we've been and asked them nicely,
They informed us, quite concisely,
Just what we could do precisely, all through the night.

Roy and Pearl were newly-wedded, all through the night;
To the wedding bed they headed, all through the night;
Though at first he failed to suit her,
She has proved an able tutor;
Now they do the Kama Sutra, all through the night.

In the Old Goat Inn they're drinking, all through the night;
Whatever is the landlord thinking, all through the night?
Though it's almost half-past four,
He's not worried 'bout the law:
They'll be calling out for more, all through the night.

Mrs Dace sits by her curtain, all through the night;
She'll know what goes on, that's certain, all through the night;
Poachers, lovers, thieves and debtors,
Those who really should know better,
She is writing blackmail letters, all through the night.

When Sir Hugo raped and pillaged, all through the night;
He was the scourge of all the village, all through the night;
He thought he was such a joker,
We thought his wit mediocre;
Someone stuck a red-hot poker, all through the Knight.

SID KIPPER SAYS: *"This song should be sung slow, so that people can join in. Although, if you're on your own you can sing it as fast as you like."*

The second part of the 1940s was all births and deaths. I don't recall any marriages. Unless you count Cyril and Cynthia Cockle. Most people don't. If you did the answer would be two.

In 1946 my Ruby gave birth to Annie. At least, she said she did. I wasn't there. It wasn't done in those days. It was women's things, so men weren't welcome. I remember the midwife coming round when the time came. "Best you go out Mr Kipper," she said. "You'll be no use here." So I had to wander the lanes. It was a bit awkward really. I'd never loitered without intent before. Eventually word came that it was all over and I went home. And there was this child. So I assume Ruby gave birth to it. But I'd no real evidence.

While I was wandering the lanes I ran into my brother Henry. He was doing the same as me. Because that very same night his wife Dot claimed she gave birth to a boy. Sid. Now, there's a lot been said. There's been aspertions cast and nods winked. Hints dropped. So let's clear this up once and for all. No more bush-beating. No more going round the houses. Sid could very well be my boy.

How it came about was like this. It was New Year's Eve 1945. I was out doing a bit of pheasant collecting. It was the perfect time. All I had to do was black up my face, carry a piece of coal and put on a Scottish accent. That way people would leave me alone. Just after midnight I was slipping round the back of Box Cottage. That's where Dot and Henry lived. Henry was out, and Dot had been drinking. As I slipped past the door opened and she called out: "Is that you, Fritz?" Fritz von Scmidt was their Scottish border. Big on ballads, he was. "Och aye," I said. "The noo." I'm a master of disguise. So Dot called me to come in and keep her company; "Like you usually do when Henry's out." I couldn't see a way out so I stepped in. "Is that a piece of coal in your hand," she said, "or are you just pleased to see me?" Before I knew it one thing led to the other. We rubbed each other up the right way. It took me back to our honeymoon. When we'd done she said, "Off to your room now, you naughty Scotsman." So I left. I don't think she recognised me. Even though Fritz had a scar on his cheek, wore a monocle, and walked with a limp. I met him on the way out. Said he'd been bird-watching. Used to do that a lot. Round the airfields. He was a harmless enough bloke, even if he did like goose-stepping in his tartan jackboots.

I got home just in time to meet Henry leaving my cottage. I didn't say anything. We still weren't talking. Ruby said he'd been passing, and dropped in to borrow a cup of sugar. He must have eaten it on the spot, because he didn't have it when he left.

Then, like I say, Sid and Annie were born on the same day. Saturday. So you can jump to your own conclusions. I mean, when you come to it you never know, do you? You just have to take a woman's word for it. For all I know the babies could have been swapped at birth. All I'll say is it's pretty clear which block Sid is a chip off. And it's not Henry's.

To balance things up there were two deaths. In 1947 Uncle Albert's wife Betsy passed on. She was only 41, but she'd packed a lot in. And I don't mean she'd given it up. It was the ghost she gave up.

The next year it was my old father's turn. After the way he'd treated me I wasn't too bothered. Nor was anyone else. He'd fallen out with just about everyone. In fact, they reckon he died of a surfeit of nothing. I went along to the Chapel of Rest to pay my last disrespects. Then it was back to the house for the reading of the will. And ham sandwiches.

The only thing he left that anyone wanted was his song-books. They certainly didn't want the ham sandwiches. They'd been handed down in the family from funeral to funeral for generations. There were two song-books. In them were all the old songs that Billy had noted down over the years. At that time I wasn't singing much, so I didn't really need them. But I was buggered if Henry would get them both. But in the end Father did the decent thing. I got the red one, and Henry got the blue one.

I went home with mine and leafed through it to see what I'd got.

DO YOU KNOW KEN PEEL?

Do you know Ken Peel at the break of day? Do you know Ken Peel in his coat so grey? When his horse and his hounds are far, far a - way, He's a - sleep in his bed in the morn - ing. For the sound of his yawn can be heard from his bed, And the cry of his hounds, which have not been fed; Their hull -a -ball -oo would a - wak -en the dead, But it won't wak -en Ken in the morn - ing.

I got a lot of good stuff from father's red book. There were ballads. Chorus songs. Children's songs. All sorts. And the old bugger had been keeping them to himself for years.

The stuff I got was more newer than older. Henry got a lot of that out-of-date stuff. Like 'Dost Thou Goeth, Pretty Damsel?' I had things like 'The Sisters of Percy', and 'Do You Know Ken Peel?'

But the songs weren't my main concern. I was busy getting business going after the war. Of course, the scrapping was over. Although I still had some to sell. But there was the spiving to take it's place. That meant hanging around street corners, in places like North Walsham or Cromer. You had to have a suitcase, a moustache, and one of those special spiv's hats. You could get them all in Woolworths. And if you had those you could flog anything off, and people thought they were getting something special. So I used to sell stuff that wasn't even illegal, for twice what it cost in the shops. And people were pleased to get it. Well, it's human nature.

It was a perfect set-up. I'd broken no laws, but my customers thought they had. So you could flog any old rubbish and they daren't complain. Even the other spivs didn't mind, because I wasn't competing with them. They had stuff like petrol coupons and nylons. I got some for Dot. Petrol coupons, that is. Shame we didn't have a car.

Then, by the end of the 1940s, rationing was being phased out. Things settled down. I amalgamated my various lines under the name 'George Kipper Enterprizes'. I got the spelling from a Yank. It had a ring to it. There were War Surplus deals. Game supplies. A bit of this. A bit of that. Yes, and a bit of the other. I was still in my early thirties, after all.

Do you know Ken Peel at the break of day?
Do you know Ken Peel in his coat so gray?
When his horse and his hounds are far, far away,
He's alseep in his bed in the morning.
    For the sound of his yawn can be heard from his bed,
    And the cry of his hounds, which have not been fed;
    Their hullabaloo would awaken the dead,
    But it won't waken Ken in the morning.

Do you know Ken Peel – well, if you do,
You can tell him from me that it just won't do.
We want to hear his view halloo,
Not the sound of his yawn in the morning.

There was Dido, Fido, Bonzo and Spot,
There was Candy and Sandy and Dandy and Dot,
There was Gandhi and Randy and Lancelot,
But they're all going hungry in the morning.

Do you know Ken Peel – he looks a fright;
He's finally found his Mrs Right.
She's his delight on a Friday night,
And again on a Saturday morning.

Do you know Ken Peel with his throbbing head;
With his streaming nose and his eyes so red?
Peel's vindaloo would awaken the dead,
But 'twill take its revenge in the morning.

SID KIPPER SAYS: *"Ken Peel was a famous huntsman round our parts. Only he didn't hold with early starts. He reckoned the early bird got the worm, and who wanted to get worms?*

His biggest cricket was a bloke called Wild Oscar. Now, that don't matter in itself, except he took to coming round our way at various times. And that needn't have mattered either, except he kept coming out with witty sayings. Well, it got on your nerves. You'd be having a normal conversation about the weather, or what Mrs Dace reckoned Farmer Trout said about Carol Cockle's handbag, and he'd just let one go. He'd draw himself out to his full width and say, 'To lose one handbag is unfortunate. To lose two looks like carelessness!' Or you'd be having a quiet pint of Old Nasty in the Goat, and he'd make a big entrance and say, 'I have nothing to declare but my duty free!' Well, aside from the fact no one knew what he was on about, it was a flipping nuisance.

But the most trouble he caused was about the fox-hunting. Now, I don't know where you stand on hunting. I sit on the fence myself. Well, you can see most of the action from there, and you're handy for the pub without getting your shoes dirty. Anyhow, years ago Wild Oscar was sitting on the same fence, watching the hunt go by, and he turned to his mate and said, 'Fox-hunting is the unspeakable in full pursuit of the inedible!' Well, this time he'd really done it, because he was overheard by Widow Hake. Well, she was a hunt follower. She'd follow anything, as a matter of fact, but she had a soft spot for the hunt. I won't tell you where it was. She was most put out, and she decided to prove him wrong, whatever it took. And that's exactly what she did. It took a while, but in the course of time she created a marvellous recipe for curried fox! Suffice it to say he was forced to eat his words. And he didn't like it. So after that he stopped coming round our way with his witty sayings. So, like he used to say – 'All swell that end swell'."

THE WIDE MISS AUDREY

Now first we strip her, then we scrub her;
We see sights to make you shudder,
Amongst the whalebone and the blubber
Round the wide Miss Audrey!
    Way-hay and up she rises,
    Way-hay and up she rises,
    Way-hay and up she rises,
    Earl Eye in the morning.

Heave up, me girls, and take the strain;
It's heavy labour, in the main,
To tighten stays and progress gain
Around the wide Miss Audrey!

Miss Audrey, when she's fully rigged,
Looks trim as any racing gig;
But we know where the cargo's hid,
Around the wide Miss Audrey!

I thought I heard Miss Audrey say:
"Just one more heave", but I say "Nay;
We're only half-way round the bay",
Soft ground, the wide Miss Audrey!

To raise her up is all our passion,
She'll have more than nature's ration;
Bristol shape and airship fashion,
Round the wide Miss Audrey!

Now up she rises at the prow;
They're line abreast and outward bound;
Where once was nought now two's a crowd!
Endowed, the wide Miss Audrey!

Tie her off, me girls, our pay we've earned;
But if she's fast we won't be sure,
Until the wind blows from her stern!
Around the wide Miss Audrey!

Now she's tight as any drum,
The tide will flow when she's undone;
But till then she'll have all the fun.
Confound the wide Miss Audrey!

Just one more task and then we'll go;
To haul them up to down below;
They're far from brief or scanty though,
All round the wide Miss Audrey.

SID KIPPER SAYS: *"There's two versions of this song, and this is the other one. Oh, and Earl Eye is the one from Suffolk, not the one from Cambridgeshire. He's more of an evening person."*

1951 started badly. Business was slow, Ruby was watching me like a hawk, and Uncle Albert died.

Albert was a real nautical character. He had a wooden leg, and a parrot. It was called Captain Smellit. The parrot, that is. Not the leg. The leg was called Smith. Albert got Smellit from 'Fly-Away' Peter, who lived over on Hughie Green. Peter bought him because he was lonely. Well he was even lonelier afterwards. Because the parrot used to sit on a perch, just inside the front door, and if anyone called he used to tell them to bugger off. That's why he got rid of it.

Aunt Betsie hated that parrot. She reckoned it taught Albert bad language. Well, she could talk. Anyway, you don't learn about lousy lubbers and vast behinds living over on Hughie Green, do you? Albert was pretty much a fixture in the Old Goat. People used to hang their coats on his leg. He had loads of stories and songs about the sea. He even wrote a couple of books. I found a copy of his *Ship Fashion and Bristol Shaped* in the library the other day. Some bastard had bent the corners back.

Mind you, Albert's taste in reading wasn't usually all that high. I remember he subscribed to Playbouy. That's a dirty magazine for sailors. With explicit pictures of ships with their sails off, and boats' bottoms. That sort of thing.

Albert ploughed the raging main. Then he harrowed it. Finally, he spread muck on it. God knows what he was up to. And he came out with nautical wisdom all the time. Like 'Any wind in a calm', and 'A tack is the best form of defence'. He said they made you think. Well, they did. But not what he thought you were thinking.

Back in 1951 Ruby was giving me a very hard time. And it wasn't fair. I mean, anyone could have a pair of ladies frillies found in their pocket, couldn't they? Especially when they've been selling ladies frillies in Fakenham all week. I used to wonder. Why is bra singular, while knickers are plural? Never mind that, said Ruby; I'm sure you don't sell used ones, like these. No, I said, but these were returned as faulty. Don't give me returned as faulty, said Ruby. I know you George Kipper. You've never done returned as faulty in your life.

Well, she was right. Except in this one case. Only I couldn't tell her that. You see the lady in question had found the knickers didn't stay up. Not when I called on her to see if she was satisfied, they didn't. She was no lady, either. But Ruby couldn't know any of that. She was guessing. She had no real proof. But I knew she was keeping a close eye on me. She told me so.

As for business, things were very slow. All the post-war fiddles had just about run out of steam. Lord Silver-Darling had a new gamekeeper who was a bit tricky, so I was keeping my head down. There was some folk-singing work on the radio, but they said I was too young. It was time for George Kipper Enterprizes to start something new.

The holiday-makers were coming back, after the war. There were loads of them, all with their spending money. So I borrowed a camera, and set myself up on Cromer promenade, taking people's pictures. It was two bob a go, or three bob with the monkey. Of course, I hadn't actually got a monkey. So I used my daughter Annie. She was quite convincing, with some make-up and a couple of rabbit skins. Especially since the pictures were so poor. People really took to her, and I made a mint. That was just selling on the bananas they gave her. I tell you, I could have sold that talking monkey a hundred times over. I might have done, but I knew Ruby wouldn't wear it. She thought Annie was playing on the beach while I took the photos.

It was a great summer. Loads of money. Sun and sea air. Lots of girls on the beach to watch. Of course Annie cramped my style a bit there. Which was probably just as well. Because you're very exposed on Cromer beach, and Ruby could have been anywhere on the cliff top with a pair of binoculars. I ended the season with a nice little nest egg. And a note from Cromer Urban District Council telling me they'd banned the use of live animals, so don't come back next year. Ah well. Easy come never kept fair lady.

CHEAP DAY RETURN TO HEMSBY

Did-n't we have a mise-ra-ble time the day we went to Hems-by? Aunt-ie was sick on the train go-ing there, and Un-cle was sick 'cos she used his lunch box. We had de-cid-ed to miss all the crowds, so we went on a Wednes - day, In - to the pub, by the time we came out the world spun round.

Didn't we have a miserable time the day we went to Hemsby?
Auntie was sick on the train going there, and Uncle was sick 'cos she used his lunch box.
We had decided to miss all the crowds, so we went on a Wednesday,
Into the pub, by the time we came out the world spun round.

Off to the beach for a bit of a swim, but we didn't have any costumes.
Pa went in in his underpants, and when he came out they were totally see-through!
As he ran round to try and dry off he frightened all of the donkeys,
As they stampeded they knocked us all down, and the world spun round.

Now for some chips to soak up the beer, afterwards we read the papers.
Taurus the bull would go on a trip, but Cancer's future was shrouded in grease.
Ma said that's daft, that's Saturday's news, Pa said mind your own business,
He shouted at her, she shouted at him, and the world spun round.

On to the pier for a breath of fresh air, Uncle went on the amusements,
Aunty was sick 'cos he lost half a knicker, when she found out which half she was even sicker!
Pa took Ma in the tunnel of love, he said, "That'll bring back old memories";
By the time they came out she had blacked both his eyes, and the world spun round.

Jill was sixteen, not used to the drink, so she went for a lay down,
Took off her dress and lay on the sand, went to sleep till a quarter to six.
When she woke up she had drawn quite a crowd, 'cos she'd forgotten her swimsuit,
She was red in the face, and everywhere else, and the world spun round.

Six o'clock, they're open again, we dragged Ma out of the bingo.
Seventeen pints of Old and Nasty, then we weaved our way to the station.
Auntie was sick on the train going home, but this time out of the window,
We were still in the station, the porter got mad, and the world spun round.

You know I think I'm getting the hang of this writing. Nothing to it. Mind you, the warder says my sentences are too short. What does he know? Let's see him do it. Words are cheap. Punctuation is free.

I started back on the singing a bit. Well, Len could look after Annie now. It was just a matter of keeping her from climbing trees, and stopping her searching herself for lice in public. I went round a few of the pubs. But there wasn't much in it beyond the odd drink. The speciality of the house in the Waggoners Walk in Antingham, I remember, was distinctly odd.

I was also looking for somewhere to invest all the money I'd made. I wasn't going to make the mistake of putting it in the bank again. There was always the Post Office. But that would have meant Beryl Bloater knowing a lot more about my business than I cared for. Not that she couldn't keep a secret. It's just that she couldn't keep it secret that she was keeping a secret. She'd drop tiny little hints to people. And of course people would fill in the details for themselves. It's amazing what people can come up with, given the smallest hint and a free hand. Cyril Cockle once told old Bloater what he was buying his wife for her birthday. And he asked her to keep it a secret. Well, by the end of the week half the women in the village weren't talking to him. They'd cross over the road and say "Disgusting", just loud enough for him to hear. The other half took to winking at him. Asking if he'd like to drop in and see to theirs as well? And he was only buying Cynthia a sink plunger.

I had my eye on buying some bricks and mortar. Preferably stuck together to make a building. I thought I could do it up and let it out to trippers. I told that to the warden the other day. He wanted to know why I wanted drug addicts as tenants.

The place I had in mind was what they call 'Ideal for first-time buyers'. That means it has got a roof, but don't expect it to keep the rain out. I went to the seller and made him an offer, cash in hand. It was quite a haggle. Because he wanted a cheque. "It's the modern way, Mr Kipper," he said. "Besides, one has to be suspicious of such large amounts of cash." Well, I told him my cash was legal, and it was tender, and that was all he needed to know. I said he could take it or leave it, but if he left it he'd be sorry. He took it.

So now I was the owner of See View Cottage. It had a marvellous rear view over Demons Wood, which could be very handy. It was a discrete way in. But first I had to make the place fit for holiday-makers. At least that meant I didn't have to work to a very high standard.

It had stood empty since old Ethel Eel passed on, the previous year. She hadn't had anything altered since before the First World War. She didn't hold with new-fangled stuff. Reckoned electricity would never catch on because you couldn't smell it. Not like horse dung, which was how she heated the place. So I had a fair bit of work to do.

I fixed the roof first, and worked down. All that winter I slaved away. Wiring. Plastering. Painting. In the end I had to take myself firmly to one side and give myself a good talking to. This is like real work, I said. Like having a proper job. And you know what you've always said about getting a proper job, don't you? Well, of course, I did. What I've always said is that if you ever feel like getting a proper job you should get on your bike. And keep pedalling till the feeling wears off.

That set me thinking. I thought if I let the house to trippers I'd have to keep working on it. Doing repairs. Redecorating. Looking after the garden. It was like a life sentence.

So I sold it instead. To the Widow Hake. I made a jolly good profit on the deal. Which only left one problem.

They paid me in cash.

MY GRANDFATHER'S COCK

My Grand-fa-ther's cock was a Rhode Is-land Red, It was hatched on the day he was born. It cock-a-doo-dle-dooed just as he went to bed, And it made a great row till the morn. It had crowed be-fore dawn eve-ry day since he was born, Till he was a com-plete ner-vous wreck, But it stopped, dead, ne-ver to crow a-gain, When he wrung it's neck. Nine-ty years with-out slum-ber-ing: *Cock-a-doo-dle-doo!* That cock ne-ver ceased to sing: *Cock-a-doo-dle-doo!* But it stopped, dead, ne-ver to crow a-gain, when he wrung it's neck.

I buried the money. I won't tell you where.

Business was doing alright. I was up to the usual stuff, plus I had a new line in show business. Not singing. Nobody wanted to hear my sort of singing at that time. Except in Antingham, perhaps. No, I was running barn dances in local halls.

All it took was a gramophone, some records, and a book of instructions. Which I sent off for. I called out the instructions, and people did the dances. I was called 'a caller'. More important, people paid to come in. I let Sid have the lemonade concession. Well, he had to start somewhere. He did a couple of Jimmy's old music-hall songs in the interval, in his little piping voice. It certainly made people glad to hear the records again.

Of course, there were always those who wanted to carp. Colin Carp in particular. He said why didn't we do the traditional dances? The local ones. Like the 'Peeing Tom Dance', and the 'Ever Decreasing Circle'. I said nobody knew them anymore. He said he did. I said alright, he could go off and do them on his own if he wanted. He said he'd do better than that. And he did. He got some musicians together, and it turned out that everybody did know the old dances after all. And they had these very popular dos in real barns. But, worst of all, they were free. Now what way is that to do business?

So that was that for the dance-hall business. But I'd made a few bob at it. I buried the money with the rest.

My Grandfather's cock was a Rhode Island Red,
It was hatched on the day he was born.
It cock-a-doodle-dooed just as he went to bed,
And it made a great row till the morn.
It had crowed before dawn every day since he was born,
Till he was a complete nervous wreck,
But it stopped, dead, never to crow again,
When he wrung it's neck.
    Ninety years without slumbering: [spoken] "Cock-a-doodle-doo!"
    That cock never ceased to sing: [spoken] "Cock-a-doodle-doo!"
    But it stopped, dead, never to crow again, when he wrung it's neck.

In the counting of sheep jumping over a gate
He had spent many hours as a boy;
But though it be dark, and the hour very late,
His dreams he could never enjoy.
For his cock it would edge, towards his window ledge,
And there it would raise merry heck,
But it stopped, dead, never to crow again,
When he wrung it's neck.
    Ninety years without dreaming: "Cock-a-doodle-doo!"
    That cock always screaming: "Cock-a-doodle-doo!"
    But it stopped, dead, never to crow again, when he wrung it's neck.

My Grandfather said he could stand it no more,
And he must put a stop to that cock.
So he went into town, to the general store,
And he bought a tall pendulum clock.
He set the alarm, in a manner cool and calm,
Then he strode to the yard without check,
And the cock stopped, never to crow again,
When he wrung it's neck.
    Ninety years of insomnia: "Cock-a-doodle-doo!"
    He said, "Well, it gets on you": "Cock-a-doodle-doo!"
    But it stopped, dead, never to crow again, when he wrung it's neck.

The very next day it was baked in it's skin,
And it tasted just fine, there's no doubt.
With a handful of sage and an onion within,
And some nice roast potatoes without.
But then, with a moan, Grandpa choked upon a bone,
And he fell, stony dead, to the floor,
And the ghost of his cock could be heard far below,
As it welcomed it's master once more.
    So now for eternity: "Cock-a-doodle-doo!"
    He'll hear that infernal ditty: "Cock-a-doodle-doo!"
    As it crows on, never to stop again, until doomsday.

THE DISABLED SEAMAN

Oh sail-or, sail-or, will you mar-ry me, with your smile so sun-ny, Jim? Oh no, nice girl, I can-not mar-ry you, for I have no teeth to put in. So off she went to her grand-fath-er's glass, And fished out some teeth of the ve-ry high-est class, And the sail-or put them in!

SID KIPPER SAYS: *"This was one of Uncle Albert's songs. He knew loads of them until he joined the British Legion. Then he forgot."*

Over the next couple of years Ruby gradually unruffled her feathers. She stopped searching my pockets every night. I reckon she knew what I got up to. She didn't like it, but she knew. Anyway, what's sauce for the gander is stuffing for the goose, isn't it? I knew very well that the milkman didn't get paid in cash.

Don't get me wrong. We always loved each other. Never wavered. But neither of us was the faithful kind. I reckon it worked out alright. Anyway, it's none of your business.

I took to going to the Waggoners Walk quite a lot. The landlady, Big Lilly, had been a famous stripper. Nothing to it, she reckoned. You just had to learn to grin and bare it. She was full of stuff like that. She used to say that outside every thin woman was a fat man. Trying to get in. They had singing in there on a Thursday. Other nights they had other things. Monday was always a General Knowledge quiz. They had questions like "Which General, at the Battle of Wellington, slept with his sword down his trouser leg?" It was a bit specialised for me. Tuesdays was the night for pigeon fanciers, so I never went in then. I reckon that sort of thing is disgusting. I preferred the singing.

I used to do a few of the old songs. Plus one or two of my own. But I wrote them so you couldn't tell them from the real thing. Things like 'I Love Not Where I Live':

Come all you maids that think to marry, and live constant with your swine;
Let me advise you this very moment – think again and change your mind.
Quite besotted, I got knotted, ignoring the advice my mother give;
Wedding bells rang me to hell, and now I love not where I live.

    I should have heeded those who pleaded, those who said it would not work;
    That night I went to bed a bride, next morning woke up with a jerk.
    Then he roused, while I still drowsed, and tackled me most primitive;
    Quickly wedlock turned to deadlock, and now I love not where I live.

So I was in there one Thursday when this posh stranger came up to me and said, "What are you having to drink?" Well, he wasn't catching me out with that one. "I'm not having to drink anything," I told him. "I'm a volunteer." I was wary. There was something about him that reminded me of those folk-song collectors I told you about. And I wasn't far off. Because it turned out he was a folk-singer collector.

32

Oh sailor, sailor, will you marry me, with your smile so sunny, Jim?
Oh no, nice girl, I cannot marry you, for I have no teeth to put in.
So off she went to her grandfather's glass,
And fished out some teeth of the very highest class,
And the sailor put them in!

Oh sailor, sailor, will you marry me, with your rambling, rolling gait?
Oh no, nice girl, I cannot marry you, for I'm one leg short of a set.
So off she went to her grandfather's table,
And sawed off a leg that was very, very stable,
And the sailor screwed it in!

Oh sailor, sailor, will you marry me, with your pigtail down you back?
Oh no, nice girl, I cannot marry you, for it's hair on my head that I lack.
So off she went to her grandfather's chest,
And plucked him some hair of the very, very best,
And the sailor stuck it on!

Oh sailor, sailor, will you marry me, with your sparkling eye so jocular?
Oh no, nice girl, I cannot marry you, for you see I'm strictly monocular.
So she went to the marbles her grandad had lost,
And brought him a bull's-eye of the very, very best,
And the sailor popped it in!

Oh sailor, sailor, will you marry me, with your bragging and your boasts?
Oh no, nice girl, I cannot marry you, for you see, I'm deaf as a post.
So off she went to her Grandfather's band,
And brought him a trumpet that was very, very grand,
And the sailor strapped it on!

Oh sailor, sailor, will you marry me, with your great big marlin spike?
Oh yes, nice girl, I'll surely marry you, for you're just the sort of thing that I like.
So off they went to her grandfather's cradle,
And there she found out that this seaman was quite able,
And the sailor put it in!

I never got it all quite straight. He worked for the BBC. They were doing some experimental programmes. Called 'The Radio Dirges', or something like that. And they wanted to experiment on me.

Well, I suppose I was flattered. I suppose I was a bit dazzled by the attention, and all the modern equipment. I know I should have got a contract. They recorded me for hours, singing and talking. They took my photo. They encouraged me to tell them more and more about my life as an agricultural labourer. Well, I had to let them think that. It was what they wanted. So that was what I gave them. It was all for a programme called 'Trilling The Tilling'. All about the old ways of farming. Well, I could have put it all in one word. Grinding. Grinding hard work, and grinding poverty. But they wanted more, so more is what they got. I'd assumed I was on an hourly rate. It was only after they'd gone that I realised that I wasn't on any rate at all.

It was a lesson in business for me. One I already knew, really. You don't give something for nothing. There's no such thing as the free French. Still, it did them no good either. Another lot came along with a similar idea, and they were the ones that succeeded. Did a programme about fishing, with some old boy over Winterton way. But here's the thing. One of the songs the first lot recorded off me became a hit. 'The Mild Rover'. And since I'd sworn blind it was an old song, I didn't get a penny.

THE OLD LAMB SIGN

There's inns where peo-ple sit and talk, Pubs where they stand and shout; But there's a bar where most folk are Quite sil-ent, laid flat out. The Old Lamb sign, my dear, The Old Lamb sign; We'll take a cup of Blind-ness yet, At the Old Lamb sign.

SID KIPPER SAYS: *"The Lamb used to serve Bilge's Blindness, which was so strong you could only drink a cupful at a time. On New Year's Eve they used to sing this song. Then they got back to fighting."*

You may wonder how I got my current position in the library. Well, that's easy. I told them I'd been keeping books since 1956. I just didn't say what sort of books.

Back then, off-course betting was frowned on. In a strictly legal sort of way. So as I was going about from here to there, for this and that, I started keeping a book. It proved a nice little earner. Most people can't calculate the odds of the Pope being a Catholic. As Farmer Trout says, there's one shorn every minute.

I was becoming almost respectable. In a disreputable sort of way. Even then, I was surprised to be invited up to the Great Hall. By Lord Silver-Darling himself.

We'd never had much communication. Except for him shouting, "When I catch you taking my birds I'm going to flog you to within an inch of your life." That sort of communication. I didn't think he trusted me.

So I went to the Hall with some worry. But I needn't have bothered. I was shown in to him by Herring Junior, the butler. Strange bloke. "His Lordship will attend to you when he has completed the underwear inspection." Well, I've never seen the like. All the female members of staff were lined up and bent forward over the huge dining table. And his Lordship was going along the line, lifting up each skirt in turn, and peering closely at what lay beneath. "Got to make sure standards are being kept up," he said. To no one in particular. When he got to the end of the line the girls stood up, pushed their skirts down, and filed out. As if it was all perfectly normal. It was only a shame it happened on the opposite side of the table to me. Mind you, in the case of the second parlour maid he didn't see anything I hadn't already seen. And more.

"Kipper," he said. When they'd gone. "A little bird tells me you are offering a service to lovers of the turf." I didn't know what he meant. But I could see it might be a business opportunity. "If it's turf you want I could get you some. How many acres would you like?" He laughed, as if I'd made a joke. "I like you're style, Kipper. I was referring to your willingness to accommodate a wager. And if it's all the same to you I'll have two guineas on Double Sherbet in the third race at Yarmouth." I said that should be no problem. I waited for the two guineas. He saw what I meant. "I don't keep small change about the place. I'll settle up later."

Herring saw me out, and from then on I had to call at the Hall every race day. And if I happened to call during underwear inspection, well, that was all the better.

There's inns where people sit and talk,
Pubs where they stand and shout;
But there's a bar where most folk are
Quite silent, laid flat out.
    The Old Lamb sign, my dear,
    The Old Lamb sign;
    We'll take a cup of Blindness yet,
    At the Old Lamb sign.

Should old resentments be forgot,
And never brought to mind?
Should old resentments be forgot?
Not at the Old Lamb Sign!

There's those who like a game of crib,
And some who play at whist,
But at the Lamb the only hands,
Are dealt out shaped as fists.

Some wrestle with their consciences,
Some fight their faults to smother,
But faced with sin we just give in,
And set about each other.

Some places charge for extras, but
We think they've got a gall;
For herewithin it comes all-in
And often free-for-all.

So let us sing of the closing year,
And the glory that is Trunch.
Come, join your hands, for then no man
May swing a sneaky punch.

The only problem was that I couldn't tell anyone why I was visiting the Hall so often. People began to ask questions. Then they began to make up answers. Behind my back. I was having a dalliance with Her Ladyship. I was blackmailing Herring. I was having a dalliance with Herring. And so on. The devil finds work for idle minds.

It didn't really bother me, though. I've always been a man of mystery. If they thought I was doing one thing, that meant they didn't think I was doing another. Then a peculiar thing happened. My brother Henry came to see me.

We hadn't talked for years. We just did the formals. Births, marriages and deaths. Christmas and Valentine cards. So I was surprised to see him. "Mind if I have a word?" he said. "You've already had six," I replied. It wasn't a good start, but what could you expect? "I won't come in," he said. "I wasn't going to ask you to." "It's about you and His Lordship." "Is it now?" "Is what now?"

Eventually he came out with it. He was worried about the family's reputation. "The Kippers have gone backward in St Just for generations," he told me. "And all that time we've been proud to be poor. We've never had anything to do with posh people. And now here's you going up to the Great Hall all the time, and it's ruining our reputation. Carry on like this and we'll have to use serviettes and keep up with the Joneses."

Keeping up with the Joneses had never been a problem for me. I just waited till they got something new, then nicked it. Anyhow, they lived in Roughton. What had they got to do with anything?

Henry was still rambling on, though. "I've got a wife and Sidney to consider. What d'you think it's like for them, having a relative who hob-nobs with nobs?"

There was quite a lot more of this, but I didn't hear it. I'd closed the door by then. Still, he had a point. The Silver-Darlings weren't our sort. They did things we didn't. Like throwing people off their land. Foreclosing on mortgages. Getting their staff pregnant and then firing them. Posh things like that. I asked Ruby what she thought. She said he had a point, too.

Well. That was a real dilemma. Obviously something had to be done about it. But I couldn't let Henry think he'd been right. And I didn't want to lose a good customer.

His Lordship came up with the answer. Being noble he could see the sensitivity of the matter. So he had a notice made, saying 'No Hawks, Trampers or Kippers', and had it nailed to the front gatepost. From then on I sneaked in round the back. At night. Which was no real hardship, especially in the poaching season. Because I was going that way already.

BIG MUSGRAVE

A   hol - i - day, a   hol - i - day, and   all the peo - ple   dozed,   Lord

Ormes -by's wife went   in - to the town, but   ever -y - thing was   closed.

SID KIPPER SAYS: *"I can remember George launching into this one full belt, stood at the bar of the Goat Inn. He didn't half get served quick, I can tell you!"*

A holiday, a holiday, and all the people dozed,
Lord Ormesby's wife went into the town, but everything was closed.

She couldn't get no shopping done, and so she looked around,
And there she saw big Fatty Groves a-lying on the ground.

Go home, go home, you Fatty Groves, you are a drunken lout;
Go home, go home, you Fatty Groves, you should not be let out.

Oh I can't go home, and I won't go home, I can't go home for my life,
For the ring off my finger I have lost, I'll be murdered by my wife.

Well if I am quite frank with you your wife is not at home,
For she is in my husband's bed, and she is not alone.

So as I've nothing else to do, no really, not a thing,
I might as well come back with you and help you find your ring.

Now a servant who was standing there, just why nobody knows,
He swore his cronies they should hear before the pub was closed.

And when he came to the broad mill-stream he did not see the plank,
And in his hurry to carry the news he fell on his belly and he sank.

Big Fatty and Lord Ormesby's wife they hunted far and low,
But where Big Fatty's ring might be they neither of them knowed.

Big Fatty and Lord Ormesby's wife they hunted high and wide,
Till Fatty fell upon the bed, and she fell by his side.

Big Fatty Groves he got up to go and wash his face,
When he returned Lady Ormesby's husband lay there in his place.

Saying well I like your feather bed, and well I like your sheets,
And well, to be frank, I like your wife, who lies in my arms asleep.

36

It would be 1959 when His Lordship had a word in my ear. Seems he had this daughter, Iolanthe. I already knew that. Seems she was at college in London. I knew that too. And it seems she'd been along to something called a 'folk club'. Well, I didn't know that. His Lordship had a question. Didn't we used to have some of that stuff round these parts?

I told him I didn't know about that, but I'd find out. I was stalling, because I needed to know what the angles were. Where was the profit? I wrote to my boy Len. He was studying in London too.

It had come as quite a shock. We'd never had a brainbox in the family before. Higher education wasn't our thing. Low cunning was more like it. It had Henry worrying about the family's reputation again.

Len wrote back to say these folk clubs were all the rage. They were held in coffee bars. And they weren't just in London. They were starting in all the big cities.

I made a few enquiries, and found out there was one in Norwich. So I took the train and checked it out. Well, I soon realised that I wasn't going to be a famous folk-singer. It wasn't fair, really. Last time people wanted folk-singers I'd been too young. Now I was too old. What's more, I couldn't play the guitar.

But I could see there might still be something in the songs I'd got. And the ones I could get. By writing them. So I told His Lordship there was nothing of that sort round here any more. And I told Len to keep me posted.

"Stay there, stay there," said Fatty Groves, "I shall not rant and curse,
For you have got the better of me, and I have got the worse."

"Stout fellow," said Lady Ormesby's husband, taken like a man,
But in then comes Mrs Fatty Groves and in amazement stands.

Saying, "How do you like my feather bed, and how do you like my sheets,
And how do you like the curtains that I got in the sale last week?"

And up then spoke Mrs Fatty Groves, never heard to speak so cheap,
"You told me you couldn't stand your wife, but now with her you sleep."

Lady Ormesby's husband he jumped up, and ran right out the door.
"I didn't know it was her," he cried, and was never seen no more.

Fatty fainted clean away at the closeness of the call,
The ladies picked him up, and they leant him against the wall.

They leant him up against the wall, but that was a disaster,
For Fatty weighed full twenty stone, and the wall just lathe and plaster.

The wall gave way, and Fatty fell, oh Fatty fell outside,
And when he came to the broad pavement he fell on his head and he died.

"A grave, a grave," these ladies cried, to bury Fatty in,
"But better you make it extra large, or you won't get him all in."

"How typical, how typical," these ladies they did say.
"How typical of men to go and spoil a holiday."

THE BLOODY WARS

"Oh hark, the bug-le calls my love, you can no long-er stay, For the
sol-dier boys are must-er-ing, and you must march aw-ay." "But my toe-nails are in-
-grow-ing love, my corns are caus-ing strife, My bun-ions are re-volt-ing; I can't
march to save my life."

"Oh hark, the bugle calls my love, you can no longer stay,
For the soldier boys are mustering, and you must march away."
"But my toe-nails are ingrowing love, my corns are causing strife,
My bunions are revolting; I can't march to save my life."

"With all the jolly soldier boys you must march off I know,
And leave me hear to weep and mourn, in discontent and woe."
"But all those jolly soldier boys, they're miserable as hell;
Besides I've no clean underwear, so I can't go, very well."

"Oh you must cross the world my love, traverse exotic lands,
To meet outlandish foreigners, and kill them if you can."
"But I can't speak their languages, their manners are so rude,
And besides, I don't agree with all that funny foreign food."

"Oh you must don your breeches, after you have said goodbye,
For the Queen she have invited you to go away and die."
"But my waist it is too slender and my thighs they are too thin –
If I were to don my breeches, they'd undon themselves again."

"Then I'll cut all my curly hair, and dress in man's array,
And as a gallant soldier boy I'll boldly march away."
"Then you must wear my uniform – you are thicker round the waist –
And I will stay at home, love, while you march off in my place."

"And when she heard him say so, she fell down on her knee,
Crying, "Johnny, I'm with child by you, stay home and marry me."
But when he heard her say so, he cried, "Alack-a-day,
Bloody wars, the bugle calls my love, and I must march away."

SIDKIPPER SAYS: *"That's the thing with women. If you want to go off fishing, they reckon you should stay home with them. But if you don't want to go off and get shot at, they reckon you should leave at once. They'd rather you got killed than have a nice time."*

38

By 1960 business was going so well I needed to take someone on. It should have been Len. But he was busy stuffing his head. What I wanted was someone who was ready, willing, and able. But I just couldn't get all three. I tried loads of people. But they all fell short on one thing or another. Barkus was willing and ready, but not able. Mabel was able and ready, but not willing. And Ethelred was able and willing, but not ready. It was quite a puzzle.

Then Ruby said, "What about Sid? He's all three." Well, I wasn't sure. Then she clinched it: "And he's cheap." The next Monday Sid started as my apprentice. It made perfect sense. He'd already just about taken over the poaching. He had the right attitude. He might even make a half-way decent singer one day.

Mind you, taking on a fourteen year old isn't that easy. There's a lot he doesn't know. There's a lot he can't do. He can't even buy you a drink. Well, not legally. Ernie Spratt in the Old Goat didn't mind. "His money's as good as anyone else's," he reckoned. It was better than some. The Cockle family still operated by barter back then. It was a rabbit for a pint, a pheasant for a whisky, and a rat for a packet of wet-roast peanuts. If memory serves.

But I was on about Sid. He was a quick learner. He soon learned to be out of the way when there was any hard work to be done. That was the first thing I taught him. Or it may have been the second thing. I think the first thing was to always turn out smart. Take a pride in your appearance. If you don't, nobody else will. But only above the waist. Nobody likes a smart arse.

My latest venture was clothing. Not in St Just, of course. If you said menswear there they'd just say, "I know they do. The air's blue sometimes." But in the bigger places, like Cromer, and Holt, there were a few more trendy types. And they wanted their winkle pickers, drain-pipe trousers, and drapes. Those were sort of long jackets. Made out of curtains. They wanted all the latest fashions. So I used to have them run up for me. Lots of women had sewing machines, so I'd just supply the material and the patterns. Or, at least, a general idea. Of course, they'd never seen the real thing. But that didn't matter. Nor had the people buying them. So they only had to be fairly accurate.

I think we started a few fashions of our own. Aylsham may have been the only place where they wore drain-pipe trousers with one leg longer than the other. It was just how they came out. The thing about the fashion business is it's the exact opposite of normal clothing. People who buy normal clothing want something practical, hard-wearing, and economical. People who buy fashion prefer clothes that are uncomfortable, shoddy, and look daft. Hard wearing doesn't come into it, because the stuff goes out of fashion before then. Of course, the mugs I sold to weren't as big as the ones in London and such like. I couldn't just think of a price, double it, then turn it into guineas. Like they could. Then again, they couldn't disappear if things got a bit hairy. Like I could. Like the time I got all those cheesecloth blouses made up without washing all the Stilton out.

But I'm getting too previous. The way it worked was like this. When I got a new line I'd get Sid to wear it around the local towns. Unless it was for women, of course. Then I'd get his young lady Raquel to wear it. They'd say it was the latest thing from London. Then next day I'd turn up with some for sale and clean up.

People are easily led. If you say it comes from London they'll buy anything. They don't stop to think. I mean, what good ever came from London. The Plague? Income Tax? The Hokey-Cokey? But people don't know how horrible London is. The streets aren't paved with gold. In fact some of them are barely paved at all. And a lot of people aren't even on the mains. It's true. I was there in the eighties, and a lot of them were forced to drink bottled water.

But if people wanted things from London, then that's what they'd get. I almost felt guilty taking their money. Almost.

FOLK ROOTS '66

Driv-ing a-long in my mot-or car; My girl say we must-n't go too far; All the way these thoughts are mine; All the way or I'm wast-ing my time. Driv-ing a-long with my lit-tle chick, on the B 1 4 3 6.

SID KIPPER SAYS: *"This song really happened. The girl ended up marrying a chicken-sexer from Hales. No good ever came of it, just like George said it wouldn't."*

One reason I wanted help was to give me more time to write songs. I reckoned with this folk stuff taking off there might be a market. And I wasn't getting any younger. The time to cash in might be now or never.

Of course, it's turned out to be something between the two. I mean, I caught the warden humming one of my tunes this morning. But when I asked him to pay me my performing rights he just laughed. Said the best things in life are free. That was one of mine too!

But that's a long way down the red-brick road. That was another one of mine. In the sixties I was just starting out in the modern music business. I knew I could write words. I knew I could write music. I even knew that when I put them together they sometimes fitted. With a little stretching here, and a little tucking-in there. Just like the fashion business, really. The question was what sort of songs would sell? When you thought about it, the field was wide open. So after I'd rounded up the cows and closed the field, I went back to thinking about song-writing.

Over the years I had a go at various styles. I did a bit of Roll and Rock, but couldn't break in. Which was a bit of a first for me. You see, to sell Roll and Rock you had to go to Tin Pan Alley, but I could never find it. I didn't even know what town it was in.

I tried Country and Western. But I was handicapped by living in the East. So some really good songs never saw the dark of night. Don't just take my word for it. See for yourselves:

I've moseyed into Wighton, made camp across at Sporle,
I've whooped it up in Spooner Row, poked cows in Gressenhall,
And every kid I meet there, I'm related to them all,
For I have made my deposit in the sperm bank of life.

Now, there's nothing wrong with that. Is there?
I tried my hands at a children's' song, but that didn't really come out how I'd meant.

I know a young lady who opened a fly,
I think I know why she opened that fly,
Oh me, oh my.

And so on. With lots of humorous stuff about what she swallowed. And things wriggling and wriggling and tickling inside her. For some reason people thought it was rude.

Driving along in my motor car;
My girl say we mustn't go too far;
All the way these thoughts are mine:
All the way or I'm wasting my time.
Driving along with my little chick, on the B1436.

She's less of a chick – more of a heifer.
She fills the back seat of my Zephyr.
She's just set me a bit of a poser;
Am I a bull or just a dozer?
She's pressing my horn, just for fun, on the B1151.

From Cromer to Californee-eye-ay
Is thirty miles, but it takes all day;
Stopping at every wayside inn –
She only does three miles per gin.
One over the eight and feeling fine, on the B1159.

Cruising along on a Norfolk Broad;
My navigation was somewhat flawed.
As a boat this car is rotten;
That's not how I thought of touching the bottom.
Hoping that I can reach the shore, and the B1354.

Shuffling home – oh what a farce;
That's the last time I mix women and cars.
My motor's sunk, and so are my hopes;
My girl's gone off with another bloke.
Walking home, half alive, on the B1145;
Don't these bus cuts make you sick?
This used to be Route '66.

So what about folk-songs? Well, I'd become a bit wary of them, some years before. Because I found they could get you into trouble. How it happened was like this. I was out one day a-walking, and I came to some mossy bank. Just like in the old songs. And I decided to throw this young maiden down upon it. Without regard to the rumpling of her gown. Just like in the old songs. Well, suffice it to say she wasn't best pleased. I was soon sadder but wiser. Just like in the old songs.

Then it came to me. What these old folk-songs needed was bringing up to date. Making them modern. So I had a go at that. I did various ones. Like 'My Love Has Got A Big Red Nose'. That sort of thing.

Nowadays everyone is at it. It's easy enough to do. For instance, take 'There Is A Tavern In The Town'. Well that's also the first line. Give or take an 'in the town'. So, to bring it up to date I'd just change it to:

There is no tavern in the town, in the town,

Now, the second line is: 'And there my dear love sits him down'. Well, he can't do that, can he? There's no tavern to sit down in. But I can nick the rhyme:

Because the brewery closed it down, closed it down,

Much more modern. Now for the third line. The old-fashioned version goes 'And drinks his wine 'mid laughter free'. So I'll go for:

So he drinks his lime and lager here at home

One more line and we've got a verse. Let's see. It used to be 'And never, never, thinks of me'. No problem.

And then he won't leave me alone.

So there's the first verse:

There is no tavern in the town, in the town,
Because the brewery closed it down, closed it down,
So he drinks his lime and lager here at home,
And then he won't leave me alone.

You just carry on like that. Until you reach the end. Of course, that's just off the top of my head. Out of my brain. It needs a bit of work, but you can see the idea.

Just one more tip, if you want to be really modern. Whatever you do, make sure the man loses out. That goes down very well with all the little ladies nowadays. Bless their beautiful bottoms.

THE BELLES OF ST JUST

The belles of St Just are really a must,
They'll ring you to bed, and then swing with a lust.
Apples and pears, say the belles of St Clare's;
They'll give you a ding-dong when they get you upstairs.

The belles of old Howe are justly renowned,
They start at the top and go all the way down.
Bananas and dates, say the belles of St Kate's;
If you want to peel them, they'll co-operate.

The belles of Methwold are brassy and bold,
You can say what you like but they will not be tolled.
Rhubarb and prunes, say the belles of St June's;
They'll soon get you going and keep you in tune.

The belles of West Darcy seem stuck up and classy,
But that's just a front, 'cos their backs are all grassy.
Gooseberries and limes, say St Caroline's;
When they start to swing they'll show you a good time.

The belles out at Watton, are never forgotten,
They're round at the top and flare out at the bottom.
Here's good luck and health to the Norfolk blue belles;
I've pulled one myself, so I'll bid you farewell.

SID KIPPER SAYS: *"The Bathing Belles were what nowadays they'd call a beauty contest. Well they would thenadays, anyway, when George wrote the song. Nowadays they'd call it a disgrace and a front to women and so on. But I'll come to that in due coarse.*

It all goes back to the time before we had the Romans. What they call BC (the C stands for 'Roman' in Latin). Back then the people round my way were the Iceni. And they used to have a custom where all the young women and all the young men of the tribe paraded around before each other. That is, in front of each other. If they were before each other they'd get ahead of themselves, and that would never do. Now, since they didn't know any better they paraded dressed only in woad. It was something to do with them choosing husbands and wives. That was their excuse, anyway. Of course, the Romans soon put a stop to all that, by killing most of them. Plus they made them choose husbands and wives for proper Roman reasons, like money.

But somehow the custom never quite died out. So it was still going some time later, when they had the Middle Ages. Mind you, by that time it was a lot more competitive. They used to do it by nude wrestling in mud. I think they got the idea from the Romans.

Then, come the Late Ages, someone went and drained the Fens, which meant that mud was a lot harder to come by. So then they went back to the idea of parading. But now they did it fully clothed. Well, as you can imagine, it nearly died out due to lack of popularity. I mean, you can see a lot of people parading about with their clothes on any day of the week, can't you? It led to a bit of a crisis, because it meant nobody wanted to get married. They reckoned they weren't going to take a risk like marriage sight unseen. So that's when the Bathing Belles as we know them today were invented.

The idea was that all the young people would go to the seaside and take most of their clothes off. To make it official on certain days they lined up all the women and judged them. And it all worked fine until the Victorians invaded. Because they had a thing about covering everything up. They even used to put frills on the limbs of trees. The countryside certainly looked different then! So, of course, all the women had to be covered up too. It got to the point where all the girls had to get behind a screen, with only their feet showing, and the judges used to ask them questions. They all used to say that they'd like to travel, and the one who said she'd go the furthest used to win. They were dark days. Although not Dark Ages. It was too late for them. Anyhow, eventually the Victorians were defeated, and after that they wore less again. First it was just a one-piece swim-suit, then a two-piece swim-suit, and then a one-piece again. Only that was just one part of the two-piece. But don't get me wrong – they weren't forced to parade topless. No, they could choose which piece to wear. And where to wear it, come to that.

My girlfriend, Raquel Whelk, was Miss Scratby in 1962. They said she was second to none. She was furious about that, because she reckoned that wasn't much to be second to.

But it all came to an end, due to people not being able to let a good thing alone. You see in 1964 the Miss Norfolk Competition was started in Cromer to attract tourists. All the villages had their own competitions, and the winners went on to the final. It was advertised all over the country – 'Miss Norfolk'. Unfortunately that's exactly what all the tourists did. After that nobody had the heart for it anymore.

Mind, there was another reason. Some people reckoned it was like a cattle market, although I can't see that myself. It's unfair to cattle. I mean, have you ever been to a cattle market? Cattle don't volunteer to go to market, and they don't go round the ring batting their eyelids, and sticking their udders out, and pouting. On the other hand if you put my Raquel and her girl friend in a pen with just straw to eat, and then prodded them round the ring with a stick – well, you'd end up with a couple of beauties alright, but you wouldn't do it twice.

Anyhow, the idea in 1964 was that the big final would begin with a parade of the Bathing Belles through Cromer, led by the Town Crier. And George wrote 'The Belles Of St Just' for him to sing."

THE HAPPY CLAPPY CHAPPY

There's a hap -py clap -py chap -py, at the church; There's a hap -py clap -py chap -py, at the church; He's a real, live cler - ic, but you can call him Der - ek, The hap -py clap -py chap -py, at the church.

In 1964 Len married Maureen Lesmorn. Mind you, it nearly didn't happen. It started at the reading of the bans. That's where they read out the names of all the pubs the groom's been banned from. It turned out Len hadn't been banned from any. Imagine the disgrace. A son of mine not even banned from the Crooked Vicar in Mundesley. I'd always assumed it was hereditary. Then it got worse. He said he wasn't having a stag party. Well, at that point Maureen said if he was going to turn out like that she wouldn't marry him for love nor money. That had him worried. Till she said she *would* marry him, for love *and* money. Then he said he wasn't having a stag party because she wasn't having a doe party. She said no, she was having a hen night. Right, he said. In that case he was having a cock night. It went alright from then on.

The same year Sid went off to do National Service. He didn't last long. One day an officer asked him where the rest of the troops were. So Sid told him. "You shouldn't have done that," said the officer. "I might have been an enemy." "Well if you are you've hidden it for the twenty years I've known you," said Sid. They threw him out as a security risk. So he came back home, and it was business as usual once more. Kipper and nephew.

In 1966 I became a grandfather. It was none of my doing. Len and Maureen had a baby, Karen. I was pleased. Until I realised that meant I was married to a grandmother. That took the gilt off the gingerbread. Still, to be fair, she had a similar problem.

In 1967 I had a business trip away. That is, I went away until the business of the missing Renoir at the Great Hall quietened down. Not that it was anything to do with me. It was just that by then Sergeant Sturgeon had arrived at the Police Station. And I didn't trust him not to try to frame me. Sid looked after the business for a while.

And then, when things had quietened down, the new Vicar turned up. Well, he was more like it. Trendy, like me. A singer and guitar player. Of course, he was a bit religious. But nobody's perfect.

The Reverend 'Call-me-Derek' Bream. Generally known as 'Call-me'. Or 'Dell the Knell'. Due to the fact that he got the church bells back going. They hadn't been rung for years, because the previous Vicar hated them. Reckoned he was entitled to a lay-in on a Sunday like everyone else. Sometimes he took the service in his nightdress. Or so they say. I wouldn't know. I've never been C of E. I've always been C of R. That's Chapel of Rest. And none of your business.

There's a happy clappy chappy, at the church;
There's a happy clappy chappy, at the church;
He's a real, live cleric, but you can call him Derek,
The happy clappy chappy, at the church.

There's Mister Lister's sister, in the shop;
There's Mister Lister's sister, in the shop;
She's never been married, but she's been Tom, Dick and Harryed,
Has Mister Lister's sister, in the shop.

There's Mother Glover's brother at the forge;
There's Mother Glover's brother at the forge;
He's not so good at welding, which is why he's now a gelding,
Is Mother Glover's brother at the forge.

There's Eric Porter's shorter daughter, at the farm;
Eric Porter's shorter daughter, at the farm;
In height she's quite abrupt – she can milk cows standing up! –
Can Eric Porter's shorter daughter, at the farm.

There are numerous humorous rumourers in the pub;
Yes there's numerous humorous rumourers in the pub;
They agree, without a doubt, that there's some funny folk about,
Do the numerous humorous rumourers in the pub,

There's randy bandy Mandy from the cafe;
There's randy bandy Mandy from the cafe;
For thirty bob, I'm told, she'll provide soup and a roll,
Will randy bandy Mandy from the cafe.

There's the Bacton lifeboat crew who'll rescue you;
There's the Bacton lifeboat crew who'll rescue you;
If I was a boat owner, I think I'd rather sink off Cromer,
Than trust the Bacton lifeboat crew who'll rescue you.

There's a happy clappy chappy, at the church,
There's a happy clappy chappy, at the church,
He's a real live cleric, but you can call him Derek;
He likes to think he's trendy, but he's more like Sister Wendy;
He sees the best in every one, so he misses all the fun,
Does the happy clappy chappy, at the church.

SID KIPPER SAYS: *"The best place to sing this song is nowhere near St Just-near-Trunch. Because one or two people aren't too happy that George wrote it. 'Pint-size' Porter says it's sighsist, whatever that is. Reg Glover says George would say something to his face if he had the balls. And Mandy Miller asked me to point out that there's been a price increase, due to decimalisation."*

TALKING POSTMAN BLUES

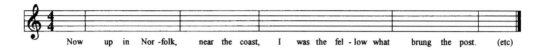

Now up in Nor -folk, near the coast, I was the fel - low what brung the post. (etc)

Now up in Norfolk, near the coast,
I was the fellow what brung the post.
But while I was the post a-bringing
I'd be playing my guitar and also singing.
That din't half craze them – that drove them doo-o-olally.

Now a whole lot of people din't like my tuning;
They reckoned their peace, bor, I was a-ruining.
But they daresn't say nothing to make me raw,
'Cos if they did I'd leave their post next door.
Lot of people got things they don't want the neighbours to know about:
They needn't'er fretted – I'd already told the neighbours everything anyhow!

Till one old woman in Northrepps, now
She say Why don't you hold your row:
Why don't you make that racket elsewhere?
I say I can't do that, I've just come from there.
Well she din't bother me none - 'cos, I'd just been discovered.
So I din't give a light, bor (now there's an idea for a song).

You see, one day this here bloke come by,
He say come along a me, I'm from the E.M.I.
I say I'll come along, and I'll do my best,
But tell me – am I under arrest?
He say E.M.I. – not F.B.I. you sorft puddin'!
I say alright but what's in it for me?
He say shut your mouth son; just sing your songs and wait and see.
Well, I may be a sorft puddin',
But I can't see how I'm going to sing with my mouth shut!

Well I made it big with my record in the shops,
And I even got on that there Top of the Pops.
I toured about, West, North and South,
And you can bet I allus opened my mouth;
'Course that weren't just for the songs to come out;
That was for things to go in too. Stardom don't half make you thirsty!

So I had my fame, and then it went,
But I always acted like a proper sort of gent.
If you want to know what I think of it,
I think that was mostly a load of old squit.
'Course I've still got my catch-phrase. Here it comes.
There it goes.
Here it comes again .... Che-e-e-erio!

Round about then a bloke I'd known on and off for years made it big. A bloke from Sheringham. Al Smethurst. He did a bit of singing, and a bit of postmanning. Wrote sort of daft songs in a Norfolk dialect. And he made it big.

We went back a long way together. And apart. We were at school in North Walsham at the same time. I remember he was a little bloke, with glasses. They reckon when they were on the train from Cromer he was the one they put up in the luggage rack.

We once wrote a song together. For the school cricket team. 'The Walsham Batting Song'. I can't recall it all. We wrote alternate lines. "Jolly batting weather": that was my line. Then he wrote, "Hev yew gotta loight roller?" And so on. I wrote the first line of the chorus I remember: "And we'll all pull together". Well, that was how we used to play. It's probably why we never won any matches. We were all caught in the deep. Uncle Albert was delighted.

So when I saw Al on the telly, singing about 'Hev Yew Gotta Loight, Boy?', I thought to myself. I thought he still can't spell. And then I thought if he could make it, so could I. Fame beckoned. Stardom called. There was only one question. Did I have to get a job as a postman first?

In the end I decided against that. That was his gimmick. I'd have to get my own. Singing Postman had been done. So had Singing Nun. So what should I go for? The Singing Bookie didn't really have it. And it gave too much away. In the end Sid came up with it. He said it would draw attention away from him. Now that he'd fully taken over that part of the business. And so The Singing Poacher was born.

My costume was a long coat with a large pocket on the inside. Mind you, people couldn't see that. That was the whole point of it. And a cap, pulled down over my eyes. Of course I didn't play the guitar like Al. Partly because I didn't have one. And partly because I couldn't have played it if I did. So it was back to the walnut-shells. And I learnt a lesson.

It's a mistake people make all the time. They see someone being successful, and they think 'I could do that.' But the thing is maybe they could. But it's already being done, thank you very much. So you're not needed. And it's twice as bad with what they call a novelty act. Because it's supposed to be novel, after all. "Just how many daft warbling buggers from Norfolk do you think the music business needs, Mr Kipper." That's what they said. The more polite ones. Then his people got wind of it, and came down heavy on me. "Certain things you might not want people to know about." That sort of thing. So that was that. Fame waved goodbye. Stardom said "Push off." Except for one thing. He started coming out with songs that sounded a bit familiar. Like the ones I'd done on my audition tape. For instance, he did 'Wass The Bottum Dropped Owt?' It sounded very like one of my songs: 'Wass The Top Come Orf?' I'd even told them some of my ideas. How I was trying to write a song about this girl from somewhere in Norfolk. I couldn't decide between 'A Hussy From Costessey' and 'A Frail From Bale'. Blow me if he didn't come out with 'A Miss From Diss'. I mean, I'd thought of that, obviously. I just didn't think it worked. I still don't. But I couldn't prove a thing. And anyway, who was I to complain about being robbed?

So I stuck to the day job. By now I had any number of irons in the pie and fingers in the fire. Ruby was in charge of fashion, selling flared trousers and daft military jackets. Sid handled the betting business. And several of his female customers, I gathered. There were all sorts of deals in various things. Len was in it by then, in charge of transport. With his lorry. When he wasn't doing his other business. Abstract painter and decorator. Which was most of the time. All that education had done him no good, it seemed.

The consequence was I was burying cash on a regular basis. If things went on like this I'd have to buy some more land.

THE SISTERS OF PERCY

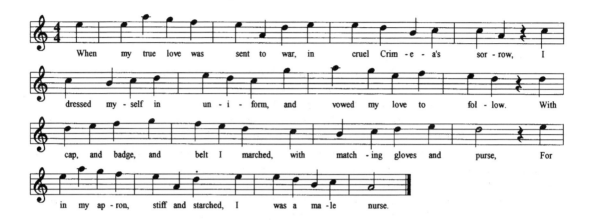

When my true love was sent to war, in cruel Crimea's sorrow,
I dressed myself in uniform, and vowed my love to follow.
With cap, and badge, and belt I marched, with matching gloves and purse,
For in my apron, stiff and starched, I was a male nurse.

One night as we prepared for bed this young nurse she confessed
She had a yen for me, she said, deep in her ample breast.
She said, "My dear, my heart you've won, all stiff and starchéd so."
I whispered, "Oh, but I'm a man"; she said, "I do hope so."

She threatened to expose me, so, not thinking any harm,
I did just as she told me, and I nursed her in my arms.
"And now," said she, "let down your hair, now take those stockings off,
And when I put my hand just there, there is no need to cough."

But my secret she revealéd, her sisters she did tell,
So to keep the truth concealéd, I nursed all of them as well.
With twenty maids to cover, oh, I thought to fail I shall,
But thoughts of my true lover served to stiffen my morale.

Now sweethearts can be fickle; when my love at last I saw,
Her heart did not beat quicker, she din't want me any more.
I asked with words profound what had caused her love to fade;
She said 'twas when she found I chose to dress up as a maid!

Well, then I was in great distress; if the army came to know,
They'd make me put on battle-dress, and fight the fearsome foe!
So I've stayed with the nursing trade, in linen, lace and lisle,
To think I sleep with twenty maids – and a mister all the while;
To think I sleep with twenty maids – and I smile and smile and smile.

SID KIPPER SAYS: *"My antecestor Gripper Kipper fought in the Crimea. Mind you, he fought in most places, because that was his job. He was a boxer. His catch-phrase was 'Fights like a butterfly, sinks like a stone'. He needed a lot of nursing."*

I was in hospital for a while about then. You'll want to know for what. Well, that's the point. Nobody knew.

It all started when Ruby came out in a rash. That shook everybody. Because everybody knew that Ruby was never, ever ill. Doctor Dabb knew that as well. Probably because he was somebody. So he said it must be a reaction to something. Something she was coming into contact with. He had everything checked out, but nothing could be found. So in the end he concluded it could only be one thing. It must be me causing it.

So I was sent to an isolation hospital. And lo and behold, Ruby got better straight away. Which only left one problem. What was wrong with me that had caused it?

They did loads of tests. I can't remember them all. They started off with the simple ones. I had a blood test, a breath test, and a sex test. That told them nothing. Well, no, that told them a lot of things. But none of them useful. So then I had a smear test, a screen test and an acid test. Still nothing useful. It went on and on. I remember having a litmus test, intelligence test, taste test, driving test, paternity test, river Test, and trial by ordeal. They tried everything, but none of them showed up the problem. They were baffled. They called in all sorts of experts, but none of them knew anything. In the end there was only one test they hadn't tried. It hardly seem appropriate. But there was nothing else for it. They said it was like Sherlock Holmes. "When you have illuminated the impassable, whatever remains, however impractical, must be betrothed." Something like that. So they gave me the test anyway. And I proved positive. On a pregnancy test!

It seems it was what they call a sympathetic phantom pregnancy. Where a man gets all the symptoms. Except the actual baby, of course. It happens sometimes when his wife is having a child. Only Ruby wasn't.

So now they had to find who's pregnancy I was sympathising with. They hummed a lot. Then they hawed a fair amount. And they finally came out and asked me if I'd been intimate with anyone else.

Now I'd slowed down a bit by the sixties. I didn't get around much any more. If you take my meaning. But there were one or two old flames that I still kindled. There was a married woman in Southrepps. I won't name her. Not to protect her reputation. She's long gone now. Anyhow, given the reputation she had it would only enhance it. It's just that I don't think I ever actually knew her name. We never did much chatting. Due to the fact that we knew it took her husband exactly twenty minutes to go to the shop for a paper and come back.

The other one was a widow in Walcott. I knew her name alright. It was Sarah Smelt. People were forever making jokes about it. Although Sarah always seemed a nice enough name to me. She was the opposite of the one in Southrepps. She liked to take her time about it. She liked everything slow, relaxed, and unhurried. Nowadays they'd say she was laid back, and they wouldn't be wrong. Personally speaking it was all a bit too slow and unhurried. I used to take a packed lunch and the paper. The bloke in Southrepps picked it up for me.

Discrete enquiries were made. They drew a blank. Neither of them was pregnant. So we were back at square one. Nobody knew what to do, but they said I had to stay in for observation. So I observed the television. I observed the papers. Mostly I observed the nurses. Famous doctors came and scratched their heads over me, but the dandruff cured nothing. It began to seem like a life sentence. Of course now I know it was nothing like a life sentence. But that's how it began to feel, nonetheless. And then, after I'd been there a little under nine months, my regular pregnancy test proved negative. Whatever had caused it, it had gone away. They let me go home. And Ruby no longer had any reaction to me.

So it was all over, and back to business as usual. And if Rachel Ruff came back from a long stay at her aunt's about then, a lot thinner than she went away, well. That's between her and me and the gatepost.

I'll always have fond memories of that gatepost

NARBOROUGH FAIR

Don't I know you from Nar - bor -ough Fair? Rose -hip tea and dead net -tle wine. Rem - em - ber me, I had or - ange hair? Were you once a true lov - er of mine?

HIM
Don't I know you from Narborough Fair?
Rosehip tea and dead nettle wine.
Remember me, I had orange hair?
Were you once a true lover of mine?

HER
Didn't you have an old grandad shirt?
Ginseng, lentils and dead nettle wine.
Without no collar, but plenty of dirt –
Was I once a true lover of thine?

HIM
Didn't you have a grey cheesecloth blouse?
Acorn coffee and dead nettle wine.
Between off-putting and bound to arouse –
Were you once a true lover of mine?

HER
Didn't we dance while folk-singers crooned?
Home-brewed yoghurt and dead nettle wine.
Without no rhythm, nor meaning, nor tune –
Was I once a true lover of thine?

HIM
Didn't you burn some incense and candles?
Herbal honey and dead nettle wine.
To clear the air when I took off my sandals –
Were you once a true lover of mine?

HER
Didn't I wake with you in your squat?
Magic mushrooms and dead nettle wine.
Unable to recall if we'd done it or not –
Were you once a true lover of mine?

BOTH
This Narborough Fair of which we both sing;
Cannabis, acid, and elderflower beer.
To tell the truth, I don't remember a thing –
In fact, I'm not even sure I was there!

SID KIPPER SAYS: *"Someone nicked this song for an advert a while back. They mixed it up with some other words and called it Narborough Fair/Rentakil. George never got a penny. They did send him some rat poison, but that could be taken two ways."*

In 1969 I got my first grandson. Kenneth. Known to one and all as Ken. Well, to all but not one, actually. Cyril Cockle insists on calling him Neth. It's his idea of a joke. And if that surprises you, you should see his idea of a garden.

Now don't get me wrong. Or do if you want. It's of no concern to me. But if you want to get me right, accept that there's something special about grandsons. I mean, granddaughters are fine and dandy. I love my granddaughter. Whatsername. But grandsons, well, they uphold the family name. Not like Whatsername. She dropped it to marry that bloke from East Raynham. We hardly ever see her now.

In here I hardly ever see anyone from home. Sid drops in from time to time, when he's touring down this way. The warder reckons I'm lucky. He says he sees his family all the time, whether he likes it or not. Reckons he only comes to work to get away from them. He took them on holiday to Norfolk last year. Called in at St Just-near-Trunch and checked up on Ruby. I never asked him to. Not a bad bloke. For a warder.

When was I? Oh yes. The late sixties. All those hippies and yippies and the like. Not my sort of thing, really. Chippies and clippies were what I was used to. But that didn't mean I wouldn't take their money.

So one weekend, near the end of the summer, me and Sid set off for Narborough Green Fair. With the chip van. Did I mention the chip van? Well I did now. But this wasn't like a normal chip run. Sid had painted out "Kipper's Fish 'n' Chips – stop me and fry one!" He'd got Len to paint "Kipper's Spaced Out Macrobionic Meals". In psychedelic colours. We got some strange looks going through Reepham, I can tell you. And we argued all the way. I told Sid there was no such place as Narborough Green. There was just Narborough. And it didn't have a green. It had a church, and a post office, and a pub over the river. Of course, nowadays it's got a trout farm as well. But there was no way of knowing that at the time. So I didn't mention it. Sid said that's all squit because it's the Fair that's green, not the place. It sounded daft to me. But he was the expert.

He'd done some research. What he'd found is that the people at these dos didn't eat normal English food, like you and me. They didn't eat spaghetti bolognaise and goulash. They ate what they called "hole food".

We were quite a hit at the Fair. The mushy peas went well. So did the deep-fried lentils. The only real problem was cooking the chips. Because you couldn't actually cut the potatoes up, so they took for ever to fry. But that paid off, too. Because by the time they were ready all the other caterers had sold out. So we sold them at a premium.

In the meantime I saw the sights. It was an education. It was enough to warm the heart of an old man's cockles. Everywhere there were beautiful people with no clothes on. Some of them were girls. I didn't know where to look. In case I missed anything. I did have one small worry. If it took off as a fashion, that'd be my clothes business out the window. Still, I knew where I could lay my hands on some bulk sun-tan lotion.

We went home tired but wealthy. We'd sold everything we'd taken. Then bought more in Downham, and sold that too. And all at prices that would have got you laughed at in Reepham. Plus we'd made a lot of friends. I don't think anyone at that whole Fair slept alone. Nobody who slept with me did.

I don't remember it all, because I had a fair bit to drink. And people kept giving me funny tasting roll-ups. I did know it had changed my whole life. Next year, I told Sid, we'll be doing a whole summer of those sort of events. I've never minded mixing business with pleasure.

My dream was short-lived. Of course. Because next year the seventies arrived.

AWAYDAY

Aw - ay - day, aw-ay - day, lo-co in tran - sit; Om -
- ni - bus, St Pan - cre - as, Aw - a - ay - day. Cle - o - pat - ra
vir - gin - ae, ter - ra in - cog - ni - ta; In lo - co par - en - tis Cae - sar,
mul -ti Ka -ma Sut - ra.

SID KIPPER SAYS: *"This song is all Greek to me. Except the bits that are double-Dutch."*

What a difference a decade makes! Suddenly there were no more Green Fairs. No more hippies. I'd missed the boat. I never even got the chance to wear the sheepskin waistcoat Ruby made for me. Well, not without a shirt. It did come in handy though. It turned out I'd invented the body-warmer years before it became trendy.

So, it was back to business as usual. Sadly. I suppose that was when I finally settled down a bit. After those young, loving girls at Narborough the women around our way didn't seem quite so inviting. A bit old and stale. And a bit overdressed. Not that I stopped altogether. I still had the odd dalliance, but only for Ruby's sake. To keep a bit of spice in the marriage. Well, it was only fair. You need to make an effort now and then in a marriage.

For a couple of years I put all my effort into the business. I did very well. A bit too well, in fact. Because next thing I knew the taxman began sniffing around. It was easy enough to spot. I'd been surveilled before. By people who knew what they were doing. So a bloke in a bowler hat with a briefcase was rather obvious. Even when he did try to hide in a hedge. But then a letter arrived. Could I explain why I seemed to have no visible means of support? Why didn't I pay any income tax? Would I like to pay some?

What sort of person did they think I was? Income tax was for people who had income, wasn't it? Whereas I was a businessman. But I asked about a bit. Nevertheless. And that's when Len's education finally came in. He looked into it all. In books. And he came back and strongly advised me to go bust.

Well that's a word I'd always been fond of. But apparently it wasn't as simple as that. Apparently it had to be done the right way. Because they wouldn't just take my word for it. However fond of it I was. There'd have to be an investigation. Which I suppose must be a technical term for looking at my investments. So we'd have to make absolutely sure there'd be none for them to find.

First I had to move my liquid assets in case they dug about near to home. Liquid assets is what they call cash. Not the beetroot and ginger wine I'd laid down. Made by Henry's wife, Dot. You only picked that up once. Then you laid it down immediately.

Awayday, awayday, loco in transit;
Omnibus, St Pancreas, Awayday.

Cleopatra virginae, terra incognita;
In loco parentis Caesar, multi Kama Sutra.

Troilus et Cresida, cum homo errectus,
Strangulated hernia, coitus interruptus.

Gina Lolabrigida, osteo arthrytus;
In vino veritas, Peter Dominicus.

Cosa Nostradamus est in video nasti;
In dramatis personae, my little poni.

Figaro in opera, minus a soprano;
Allegro castrati – Dame Placido Domingo!

Romulus et Remus in flagrente delecte;
Honi soi qui mal y pense, Harry Belefonte.

Non compos mentis, continuo ad nauseum;
Ad lib, etcetera, quad erat demonstrandum.

So I got hold of a bit of land. Over the border in Trunch. It was so far over the border it was almost over the next border. It was nearly in Mundesley. But not quite. That would have been going too far. Pit Piece it was called. Tucked away in a corner between two roads and a deep ditch. But here's the clever bit. Technically I didn't buy it. Len explained it all. He said if I bought it, then it would be an asset. Whereas if I rented it, then it would be a liability. But, of course, I needed to be sure of it, if I was going to bury my money there. So Len made up this contract. Marvellous it was. Full of parties of the first part, and heretoafters. It said I promised to rent the land for twelve years, and they promised to rent it to me. Then it said that after that I promised to buy it, and they promised to sell. Well, as you can see, that was quite a liability. Twelve years rent. Plus buying the land. I'd certainly go bust soon enough that way!

So the thing was all signed, and sealed, and tied up with pink ribbon. Once that was done Len, Sid and I dug up my money one night. We loaded it on to Len's lorry, and buried it again in the new land. It had to be done nice and quiet. After all, that money didn't exist. So it couldn't make any noise. The only person we saw was Cyril Cockle, but he didn't bother us. He was too busy trying to hide behind a tree while throwing pheasants away. So it seemed we'd got away with it.

Until a couple of days later. I was up at the new land. Making the sheep feel at home by worrying them, when a bloke called out to me. He said he was from Mundesley Council. He said would I like to explain why there'd been digging on the site. I said no, because I was in Trunch. So it was nothing to do with him. That seemed to settle it. Until a couple more days later. When another bloke, very similar, came and asked the same thing. Turned out it was his brother. Only he was on Trunch Council. Well, that was more of a problem. How could I explain it? Then I remembered a story I'd heard from a mate of mine. Mark Wide. So I said to this bloke it was alright, because I was digging for gold. He went off happy enough, then, and I thought that was that. But it wasn't.

Another bloke turned up another couple of days later. They seemed to have a thing about couples of days, these blokes. He said he was from the County Council, and his brother had told him I was digging for gold. That's right, I said, I was. And did I find any, he wanted to know? No, I didn't. I see, he said. And why did I expect to find any in the first place? Well, I said, when I rented it the bloke told me it was a little gold mine. Now I knew better.

Well he looked me up. He looked me down. He looked me side to side. And I could see what he was thinking. He was thinking this is just a daft old idiot. He's soft as a brush, but he's basically harmless. That's what he was thinking.

Which was just as well. Because that's exactly what I wanted him to think. Off he went, probably for a family reunion. And nobody from any council ever bothered me about it again. Perhaps they simply ran out of brothers.

And so I went bust. I couldn't tell the difference, to tell the truth. I just put 'Foundered 1972' after 'George Kipper Enterprizes' on my business cards. And carried on as usual.

BIKER BILL

If I had enough of Penny, I would go and call on Gilly, and
I would take her for a ride, the bonny lass upon my pillion.
    Biker Bill and Walter Shaw, jollier lads you never saw;
    Biker Bill and Walter Shaw, jollier lads you never saw.

When first I went down to the pits my bike was all in little bits;
Then came my mate Walter Shaw, he's the one who tunes my Harley.

Walter was worth his weight in gold – that's more than two hundred pounds;
Did a skid without a lid – now he's only half a crown.

When I started in this racket, I had no boots, nor leather jacket;
Now I've gotten two in fact, with 'Durex' printed on the back.

If I had another gill then Penny wouldn't ride with me;
She hates it when I drink and ride – she told me "I love a man T.T."

Walter Shaw he had a pig, he hit it with a shovel and it danced a jig;
Now he has been put away by the man from the RSPCA.

SIDKIPPER SAYS: *"This song shows you the dangers of motor bikes. Mother always says that riding them shakes all the sense out of your ears. Cyril Cockle has ridden one all his life, and it shows."*

Oh, there was some technical stuff. But that was mainly about me not having a bank account. Well, that was alright by me. It was nice to make it official.

Going bust took up a lot of my time in 1972. But a lot of other things happened as well. My second grandson, Kevin, was born. Named after some footballer, according to Len. I didn't know what things were coming to. I do now. And I can't say I'm happy about it.

The warder says that football is the new rock and roll. Well, I still prefer the old rock and roll. You can't dance to football. Even if you do still get the sex and drugs.

Not that I didn't play a bit myself. I was a handy left-half for Trunch Tornadoes. We were quite a side. Made our mark. Mainly on the opposition's shins. I wrote a counting song, going through the team. I forget most of it. I do remember it went One, the County Cup. There was also Six, a parrot. Stuff like that. You'd have to hear it.

Another thing in 1972 was a letter from a bloke calling himself Ashley Hutchings. He said he was in charge of something called 'folk-rock', whatever that was. Sid has explained it to me since. Which made it clear as mud. Anyhow, this bloke said he was doing a record of English dance tunes. And he wanted the authentic rhythm of English folk music. Or something like that. The gist of the thing was that he wanted me to play the walnuts on it. Now isn't that just like life? Just like the real thing? Here was my big break, and I was too busy going bust to take it. I had to turn him down. So he got some bloke called Mattacks instead. And he didn't even play the walnuts! Still, there was some consolation. Nobody ever heard of him again. I did get back to Hutchings, after my finances were sorted out. But he replied that he'd moved on to something else. Anyhow, I learned later on that he only paid by cheque. If at all.

What else? My daughter Annie didn't get married again. I told her if she didn't look out she'd be left on the shelf. She said there were a lot worse things. She said people put precious things on shelves, like posh plates they never used. She said that was good enough for her. As long as she was regularly dusted.

I sometimes wonder about Annie. She doesn't seem to have much interest in men. I think she may prefer women. She certainly likes camping. Well, that's fair enough. I'm pretty broad minded. Not that there aren't limits, mind. I definitely draw the line at caravanning.

So Annie's off with the Brownies a lot. It's a bit like being off with the fairies. But with more uniforms. The only man she's ever shown any interest in is Sid. Well, given what I told you earlier, I've had to watch that. We don't want any inbreeding in our family, thank you. Look what it's done to the Cockles. Or don't, if you're squeamish. Mind you, that extra thumb must come in handy when you're hitch-hiking.

I've had to make sure Annie doesn't get too close to Sid. Well, to be fair, his girlfriend has done that. I just dropped a hint to her about it and she's been on the look out ever since. She's a nice girl, Raquel. One of the Whelks. A respectable enough family. In a disreputable sort of a way. Why Sid doesn't make an honest woman out of her I don't know. Says he's not ready for the responsibility. Says he wants to be free to play the field. I won't tell you what Raquel says. There was one other thing that year. I sponsored a motor bike. It was all part of going bust. Len reckoned I needed to show some other losses. So I had my name painted all over a mate of mine. Bill Barbel. It actually did for him in the end. He got totally confused, what with people walking up to him and calling him George. "It's not George, it's Bill." He used to shout. "Well you've got a funny way of spelling it Mr Kipper," they used to shout back. That was so as to be heard over all the revving. You get a lot of that with motor bikes. That and falling off. That's why I never took to it. Sid had one. He used to drive Henry round in the side-car. When he remembered to attach it. More than once he rode off and left Henry sitting there. Balanced on one wheel and a pile of bricks. I sometimes think he did it deliberately.

THE RIGHT WRONG SONG

Now there's wars go-ing on, and there's guns go-ing off, There's mis-siles, and fis-siles, and cock-tails Mol-o-tov, There's fight-ing, there's smit-ing, and then there's dy-na-mit-ing, But it's al-right now: I've writ-ten this song.

I was a bit late getting into protest songs. On the other hand that meant there was a lot less competition. And you know what they say about the seventies. "If you can remember the seventies, you were there."

What made me want to protest was the death of Walter Kipper. I don't know why, really. It just seemed such a waste. He'd never hurt anyone. He'd never married, either. Which may add up to one and the same thing. And he was only 81. Which is no age for a Kipper. We're known for lingering.

Walter was a quiet man. And you know what they say about a quiet man. Well, they say whatever they like. They know he isn't going to argue back. Whether he had a happy life or not I don't know. He never said. To tell the truth I don't think he ever got over being in a book when he was a child. *The Come Between*. That was the book, and that was Walter. Oh, he was disguised a bit. Augustus Swineherd, the author, changed his name to Walker. Either that or it was a misprint. Perhaps that was it. Perhaps he never got over being a misprint. In the book he keeps coming in between my aunt Maud and the young Lord Silver-Darling. They're trying to have a passionate dalliance. And she keeps having to take Walter along. He never talked about it. Then again, he never talked about anything. Maybe he just had nothing to say.

I found a copy of *The Come Between* in the library here. Someone had bent page 47.

Walter used to smoke Capstan Full Strength. Forty a day. And it never did him any harm. Apart from the racking cough. And being laid up with emphysema now and then. The warden is always on about my smoking. He's always trying to get me to quit. I've told him. You don't know your man. I'm a Kipper. And Kipper's aren't quitters!

Another thing about Walter. He didn't suffer fools gladly. He suffered them miserably. Just like the rest of us. He was a man of few words, and they were inaudible. But you could tell he was always thinking about things. You could tell that because he'd suddenly look thoughtful. Or he'd have a little smile to himself. Or a little shrug. He never did anything big.

And now he was gone. And we'd never know what he was thinking about all that time. The bastard.

All of which made me want to protest. Like I said. But I couldn't just write a song protesting about Walter, because nobody would know who he was. More to the point nobody would be able to do anything about it. He couldn't be un-crushed from underneath that steamroller. Could he? And then I thought if protest songs were no use I should write a protest song about that.

It came out as 'The Right Wrong Song'. I've brought it up to date since. Back then it was all about seventies things. Like women being unfairly treated, and black people being discriminated against. But that's all sorted out now. Isn't it?

Now there's wars going on, and there's guns going off,
There's missiles, and fissiles, and cocktails Molotov,
There's fighting, there's smiting, and then there's dynamiting,
But it's alright now: I've written this song.

There's minxes held in cages, grey squirrels running loose;
There's chicken-eating foxes which the hounds are forced to chase;
Barbarians, vulgarians, and some non-vegetarians,
But it's alright now – I've pointed it out.

There's bosses screwing workers, there's unions out on strike,
There's sweat shops, workshops, and shoe shops, and the like;
There's plutocrats, autocrats, and double-glazing bureaucrats,
But its alright now – I've put it in words.

There's cars going fast and there's jams going slow,
The trains are off the rails and the oil reserves are low,
There's pollution, persecution, and God knows the solution,
But it's alright now – I've noted it all.

There's people out on demos, there's people sitting in,
There's people fighting causes and some might even win,
While some are righting wrongs, I'm too busy writing songs,
But it's alright now – I've got it off my chest.

SID KIPPER SAYS: *"I'll tell you a story about Walter. He was quite musical, but he weren't a great singer. Well, I say he weren't a great singer, but nobody knew that for sure. He used to stand up in the Old Goat sometimes, moving his lips, with his finger in his ear, but whether he was singing or not nobody could say. Except him. And if he had no one would have heard him. Some people said he was singing, and some said he wasn't. I reckon he was just complaining about the noise.*

Of course most of the time he didn't need to be heard, because he was a man of regular habits. He never needed to order a drink, because he always drank the same thing, which was whatever he was served with. He never had to say what he wanted in Mrs Dace's Corner Shop because he had a written order delivered. I know, because at one time I used to deliver it for him. And he never said thanks.

So when he did finally speak, it was just like a normal person had shouted. Not that Walter wasn't normal, you understand. He was as normal as the next man – just as long as that was Cyril Cockle. How it come about was like this. Walter was on his way home one day from collecting his pension, which means he'd been on the bus to North Walsham. When he got off he met Widow Hake. 'Good morning Walter,' she said. Of course he didn't say nothing, but she weren't put out because she knew that was the way he was. He went along, past the road-works, when the vicar came by on his bike. 'Good morning Mr Kipper,' he cried; 'Call me Derek.' But Walter didn't call him anything. The vicar wasn't put out because he knew that was the way he was. And a bit further on he bumped into my neice, Karen. 'You want to look where you're going, Uncle Walter,' said Karen. Then she added, 'You want to look out for that steamroller, an' all.' And before anyone could do anything about it Walter was under the steamroller. And that's when he yelled his famous last words.

'Oh shit!'"

THE PUNNET OF STRAWBERRIES

One June mor - ning so ea - ear - ly, the wea - ther it was free - zing, The
rain fell down in buc - kets, and the birds were sweet - ly snee - zing. This
maid was bound for the straw - b'ry fields, when she heard a man make moan: "Oh,
who will pick my straw - ber - ries?", and she answ - ered "Pick your own". With me
P - Y - O, P - Y - O, P - Y - P - Y - O.

SID KIPPER SAYS: *"'Pick Your Own' was originally a warning to ward off strawberry rustlers, but people misunderstood, and so you get where we are today, which is here and now."*

One thing I'd never had a go at was farming. It always looked like hard work to me. But Sid had a yen to have a go one year. Nothing too serious, he said. Just some strawberries. I told him no. I said planting them's easy enough. And weeding them's not too bad. Even strawing them up is alright. But then you've got to find someone who wants to pick them for next to nothing. Sid laughed. He told me I was out of touch and living in the past. He reckoned it was the other way around now. People would pay us. I told him he was bell-ringing. That's a Norfolk term. It means I thought he was clanging my clapper.

But he persuaded me in the end, and we went ahead. Rented a bit of land. Got someone to do the planting. And the weeding. And so on. Sid oversaw it. I never actually went there. Just like a proper farmer. Then, when the strawberries were ready, Sid put a sign up and waited. And people just turned up. In droves. And sure enough they paid us for the privilege of picking our strawberries.

It was 1977. I don't know if you remember the summer of 1977. How could I know? I was away from school the day they did mind reading. So I'll tell you. As long hot summers go it was the longest and hottest in living memory. And memories live a long time in St Just. The strawberries went on and on. The people kept coming and coming. And paying and paying. Mostly women. Stripped for action. I even gave a hand myself. Not with the actual work, obviously. But what could be better than sitting in the shade of a tree with a drink in your hand watching good-looking women at work, with them every now and then coming over to you and putting cash in your hand? Even the memory of it has made me forget to punctuate!

In the end we made a very nice profit. And I had some more cash to bury. I was keen to get another crop in right away. But Sid said that pick-your-own winter wheat wasn't a goer. But we kept the strawberry business going for a few years. There were good years and bad. That's the trouble with farming. In the end I got out quick. Because I found myself going into the Old Goat Inn during Miserable Hour. To moan about the weather.

One June morning so early, the weather it was freezing,
The rain fell down in buckets, and the birds were sweetly sneezing.
This maid was bound for the strawb'ry fields, when she heard a man make moan:
"Oh, who will pick my strawberries?", and she answered, "Pick your own".
With me PYO, PYO, PYPYO.

It was a damp young farmer, a sheltering in a barn;
"Can I borrow your umbrella?" Well, she thought there'd be no harm.
So off they went together, as the floods about them fell;
She thought he was quite handsome, and he thought so as well.

So now among the strawberries they both began to pick
The fruit so ripe and fleshy, and they filled her punnet quick.
By now she was wet through, from her head down to her toes;
Said he, "Come back to my place and get out of those wet clothes."

Well, thinking no harm in it she went back to his abode;
She went into the bedroom, and she took off all her clothes.
This young man took advantage, his actions were so tawdry,
For when she came back out again he had eaten all her strawberries.

She having no new clothing, her fruits he did behold;
He said, "Put on some clothes, girl, or you'll catch your death of cold."
So she ran home in his dressing-gown, with the children all pursuing;
They cried, "Hee haw, you've lost your drawers, and we know what you've been doing!"

So come all you dark young maidens that go picking of the fruit;
Don't lend your umbrella to any selfish brute.
For if you do you'll lose your clothes, and have an empty punnet,
And no one will believe you when you say that you haven't done it.

About my buried treasure. I don't want you to think I just buried it and left it alone. I wish I had. I'd have been enjoying it now. But I didn't, so I'm not.

I dug it up regularly, and replaced the old money with new money. Well, I had to, really. Different notes came in from time to time. And so on. In the early seventies I had a bit of a panic. A word that struck fear in my heart. Decimalisation. In the end it wasn't so bad, because it only affected small change. And I didn't keep a lot of that. But after that I made sure my cash was even more up to date. It meant a lot of digging. Even Sid didn't know exactly where it was at any particular time. At least. I don't think he did.

So it was a hell of a shock when I was disturbed one night. It was just coming on dawn. I'd just finished doing a bit of 'banking'. That's what I called it. Because I'd buried it in a bank. It was just a little joke with myself. And this voice called out "Have you found it yet?" Well, a hundred thoughts flew through my head. Who was it? What had he seen? What did he mean? I stayed outwardly calm. But inwardly there was a gale warning. I went over to the fence, which was on the far side from where I'd been 'banking'. And there, large as life and half as welcome, was the bloke from the County Council.

"Not given up on the gold, then?" he said. What could I say? I tried to look stupid. It's a useful trick. "Oh aah!" I said. He smiled. "Well I admire your persistence," he said, all Council-like. "Although I suspect it's misguided." I gave him the "Oh aah!" again. "Keeps you off the streets, eh?" I went for the hat trick. And with that he called up his dog and wandered off.

I spent an anxious day. It was that one. As soon as darkness fell I went and moved the cash to another part of the bank. Just in case.

It's true what Lord Silver-Darling say. Having money is a lot of hard work and worry.

THE FARMER'S CRUMPET

Oft - times they sing a - bout the hard - ships of a far - mer's life, But
I will tell you now a - bout the poor old farm - er's wife; He may get up at six o' - clock to
go to his cow shed, But I must rise at half past five, to bring him tea in bed! I can
cook, I can clean, I can sew, I can glean, As a host - ess I am a real char - mer;
But jol - ly girls all, pay heed to my call: God help you if you mar - ry a
farm - er.

SID KIPPER SAYS: *"Some people say that my Uncle Albert collected this song from Cecil Sharp, but that's just daft. The one he got from Cecil Sharp had a lot more dirty bits. This one is based on Farmer Trout's wife, Mrs Trout. She started out as a stable girl. After she married, however, she developed into a seriously unstable woman."*

So, one way and another, I've done my share of digging. And delving. I've mixed with farmers. And their families. They're very down-to-earth types. I remember one farmer's wife over Overstrand way. She was certainly down to earth. When she wasn't up to the curtain rail. But that was a long time ago, when I still had the energy. And the handcuffs. Still, it's a happy memory. The warden can't understand why I have a little smile whenever he fits them on me. He reckons farming isn't doing well just now. Says the countryside is in crisis. Well, when wasn't it?

Back in the seventies the big thing was ripping out hedges, filling in ditches, and making bigger fields. It had a terrible effect on the crab-apple jelly industry. That was my sister-in-law, Dot. She used to make tons of the stuff. Well that had to stop when the hedges came out. Because that's where the crab-apple trees were. So there was some benefit from all that hedge ripping.

They reckoned you had to have bigger fields, to use bigger equipment, to get bigger crops. You had to have bigger farmers, owning bigger farms, to make bigger profits. Well, that was alright. But only if you were one of the big farmers. Because less hedges meant less jobs and less wildlife. It was all down to brussels, according to Farmer Trout. I didn't even know he grew sprouts!

Oftimes they sing about the hardships of a farmer's life,
But I will tell you now about the poor old farmer's wife:
He may get up at six o'clock to go to his cowshed,
But I must rise at half-past five, to bring him tea in bed!
    I can cook, I can clean, I can sew, I can glean,
    As a hostess I am a real charmer;
    But jolly girls all, pay heed to my call:
    God help you if you marry a farmer.

As he goes out to view the fields he'll whistle and he'll sing;
While I must make the beds up, and get some more logs in.
And as he pats the plough horse I furrow up my brows,
For I must tend to children, dairy, kitchen, hearth and house.

Whilst with the jolly milkmaids he's a-rolling in the dew,
To produce his hearty breakfast to the scullery I go;
And when the farmers in the dell, with all his fleecy flocks,
Then I'll be in the laundry with his underwear and socks.

As he dines in the meadow on home-made bread and cheese,
I must worm the spaniels and inspect the cat for fleas;
And as he stops to take the air upon some mossy bank,
I'll pluck and gut the pheasants and scrub out the septic tank.

Too soon the sun is going down – his labour's ended now,
So he joins those jolly fellows, that all drink down at the Plough;
Meanwhile I bath the children, then supper I must plan,
To be on the table waiting for my weary labouring man.

By the fire with pipe and slippers now he hums a merry tune,
While I attend my darning, and redecorate the room;
And when he yawns and winks at me, and says "let's hit the sack",
Well at least my final chore can be performed flat on my back!

The thing about Trout is this. Whatever it is, he's against it. He's got this organisation now. 'Bigots Against Tolerance'. They're against immigration. They're against emigration. They're against how things are now, and they're against change. They're against segregation, integration and deviation. Anything ation, really.

They sent me a Christmas card last year. That was 2002.

Dear Mr Copper,
Merry Christmas and a British New Year.
This year help keep Britain great by sitting down to a truly English Christmas dinner, of Turkey,
Swede, Brussel sprouts and French fries, washed down with China tea, and followed by Irish
coffee, Madeira cake and Brazil nuts.
Bon appétit and Joyeux Noël,
Bigots Against Tolerance.

You have to wonder.

THE MAN WITH THE BIG GUITAR

The band -its cir -cle round the town, the poor folk cower in fright, For the
ban - dit chief will cut them down, as soon as it falls night. But
see there, by the sun's last rays; a gleam of hope, the Lord be praised; He'll
make the bad guys rue the day, the man with the big gui - tar. When -
- ev - er just -ice needs a hand, wher - ev - er the weak ones are, With
just a song he'll right all wrong, the man with the big gui - tar.

The bandits circle round the town, the poor folk cower in fright,
For the bandit chief will cut them down, as soon as it falls night.
But see there, by the sun's last rays; a gleam of hope, the Lord be praised;
He'll make the bad guys rue the day, the man with the big guitar.
　Whenever justice needs a hand, wherever the weak ones are,
　With just a song he'll right all wrong, the man with the big guitar.

The factory is still as steel; the workers are locked out;
All ground beneath the bosses heel, when a cry of joy rings out.
For just then driving to the gates, comes the man who is the worker's mate,
And the bosses will capitulate to the man with the big guitar

Now women, struggle though they might, cannot achieve their aims,
For men oppose them day and night, deny them every claim.
But wait, you are not on your own; no longer weep, no longer moan;
Here comes the pleasing baritone of the man with the big guitar.

For right is right and wrong is wrong, it's simple when you're sure,
And the big guitar man sings his song because his heart is pure.
With his trusty six-string at his side – 'Who was that man?' I hear you cry;
Oh, you have just been patronised, by the man with the big guitar.

SID KIPPER SAYS: *"George wanted me to point out that this song is not about anyone in particular, so don't sue. On the other hand, as they say, if the cat fits, share it."*

I was getting a bit disillusioned with the folk-singing. I knew it was going on, but I couldn't seem to get a break. Oh, they still had a folk night at the Goat. But father would have turned in his grave. If we hadn't buried him standing up to save space. Because they didn't just do the old local songs. They sang any old thing. From any old where. Any old way. I went once or twice. But I had to take my turn with everyone else. Even Cyril Cockle. Well, he'd never have been asked to sing in the old days. When I did get a go I tried one of the old songs. They wanted to know where my guitar was. So I had a go at one of my own numbers. They said was I concertina man, then? I played the walnuts. They laughed. There was only one thing for it, then. To get on I'd have to learn a modern instrument.

Sid said he could get me a guitar and teach me to play it. I didn't even know he knew how. It turned out he didn't. So in the end we learned together. From a book. *We tried A Tune A Day,* but that was no good because we didn't know any of the tunes. We tried *Burt Weedon's Guitar Book.* That went back to the mobile library pretty quick too. And whatever Miss Turbot says it wasn't me that bent the pages. In the end we got hold of a book on playing the accordion, and worked it out from there.

It's amazing how easy it is. Once you get started. There's basically only three chords in folk music. What confuses things is they keep calling them different names. So all you have to do is go through the three chords until one of them fits. Don't be afraid to force them if necessary. If you're forceful enough you'll always get one in there.

Within a couple of weeks Sid and I had taught each other all we knew. We were ready to develop our own techniques. Now, there's only two ways to play folk-songs on the guitar. There's the quiet, gentle way, with lots of separate notes. And there's the loud, strumming way, with all the notes coming out at once. The first is called 'plinking'. And the second is called 'plonking'. As things developed it soon became clear that I was a bit of a plinker. As for Sid, well. Let's just say that he wasn't.

The thing that really made my guitar playing special, though, was when I found another chord. One that nobody else had got. I found it by accident, when I was just plinking away one day. Not really concentrating. And suddenly there it was. I don't know where it came from. I don't know what it's called. But from then on whatever I sang I put it in. There was always a place for it. Even if it took quite a lot of forcing.

Now it was time for a public outing. So I took myself down to the Goat on folk night. When my turn came I got out my guitar and spent some time tuning it. That's very important. It shows you know what you're doing. Then I went into 'The Thymes They Are A Changing'. Its about plant breeding. But that didn't matter. Because when I got to the end, not forgetting my special chord, they all cheered. They thought it was great. It was just their sort of thing. There was only one problem. As far as I'm concerned. They hadn't listened to a single word I'd sung. Well, there was a lesson there. Concentrate on the music. Which is what I did when I started going to other folk clubs. It went fine, until I got to the Cherry Orchard, in North Walsham. I'd heard they had a do there. So I called in. And guess what? There wasn't a guitar in sight. They were all having to manage without. Then I saw something that startled me. I saw Walter Pardon. From Knapton. Well, his family had always been singing rivals to the Kipper Family. And I knew he'd never even bothered to learn the comb and paper.

The people were nice enough. Eventually they asked if I'd like to perform. So I got out my guitar and gave them 'Foggy Mountain AA Man'. And they all clapped politely. But the thing was they clapped everything politely. At the end of the evening the bloke who told people when to perform thanked me for coming. But would I mind a word of advice? And then he said: "You sound like a hill-billy. We want folk-singers here."

It was only later that I learned they were folk purists. And nobody took any notice of them.

BORED OF THE DANCE

As I went down to the village hall,
I met Charlie leaning on the wall;
"Why are you standing out here, Charlie?"
"'Cos I am bored of the dance," said he.
    Dance, dance, whatever do they see
    In prancing round all the time, said he;
    I'll leave them all to do it without me,
    For I am bored of the dance, said he.

"I come to the dance with me girl," he said;
"I told her that I'd rather go to bed.
'Oh yes, I'm sure you would,' said she,
'But first you'll come and dance with me'."

"She said, 'You'll come and dance right now',
But I weren't listening when the caller told us how.
They cast left, but right I went;
They danced on, but I ended in the Gents."

"I drank with the morris men, James and John;
They drank with me as the dance went on.
We drank and we drank till it all went black –
It's hard to dance when you're lying on your back!"

Oh how she danced on the night they were wed;
She danced, he drank, and then they went to bed.
There's no more story to be told,
'Cos she was too hot, and he was out cold.

SID KIPPER SAYS: *"The Charlie in this song is Charlie Proper. He used to live in Lopham, but he doesn't now. He's dead in Dereham now."*

I did have some success at the folk-singing. I began to get a few engagements. Gigs, they call them. Here and there. In the odd folk club. Round about East Anglia.

I didn't appear under my own name, because that's not showbiz. You have to have a stage name. I won't tell you what mine was. It was never a household name, anyway. The highlight came in January 1983. I had an enquiry from a folk festival in Devon. A little place called Sidmouth. Well, it might not be the big time, but it would make me national. Even international. That's what they called it. 'Sidmouth International Festival'. I think it just meant they had some visitors from the Isle of Wight.

In fact I'd been to Sidmouth Festival before. Morris dancing. Now, don't get me wrong. It's not something I chose to do. It was in 1959. Trunch Terpsichoreans were invited to go. To demonstrate their South-East morris dancing. Eric Elver broke a finger-nail at the last moment, and couldn't go. So I was persuaded to step in. They liked the step and I got the job. So I knew it was only a small event. And not exactly racy. From memory it was mostly herbal cigarettes, and sipping sherry into the small hours of the afternoon. But, like I say, it was a national gig. But that wasn't till August. A lot could happen before then.

And it did.

In February I was notified of a tax rebate. I got on to Len. How could I have a tax rebate when I didn't pay any tax in the first place? He said it was all due to Mrs Thatcher. I said I'd never met the lady. When he explained that she was Prime Minister I did recall something about someone of the sort. A loud woman with a handbag. And an edge to her voice that could castrate pigs. That was her, Len said. She'd decided that wealthy people were paying too much tax. So she was giving them some back.

When I asked what wealthy people had got to do with me he gave me a funny look. Sort of sideways. With his eyebrows raised. "Perhaps she thinks you've got a pit of money," he said. With a heavy emphasis on the 'pit'. I'd have to think about that. Anyhow, the rebate wouldn't come until July. So I could worry about it then.

Business was doing alright. The betting side had sort of dwindled, since off-course betting had become legal. But there were still some who liked to have it brought to the door. All the other bits were steady. The fish and chip van was fine. We were doing those beef-buggers as well. You've got to keep up to date. The clothing side was moving into designer labels. Like Marks and Spencer, and C & A. Stuff like that. The drug dealing was steady.

Don't get me wrong. I don't hold with dangerous drugs. Except for alcohol and tobacco, of course. But if the Widow Hake didn't know that paracetamol was legal, who was I to illusion them? And if I hinted that George Kipper's Bronchial Chest Rub had ingredients that others didn't, well, what's in a hint? Anyway, it was true. Most chest rubs don't contain a single drop of quince marmalade. You can guess where that came from. There was no stopping Dot. Of course I didn't offer the deluxe service to everyone. I only applied the chest rub personally to a few selected customers. Well, the flesh wasn't weak. And the spirit was willing.

Meanwhile Sid was dropping hints about my birthday. In November. If you remember. Hardly anyone ever does.

"You'll be 65, you know," he'd say. "Retirement age," he'd add. I said I could take a hint. And I could give as good as I took. So how about this? "Forget it." He did, too, until events overtook us. Because he was busy, doing some dance calling. He was doing a bit of singing too. With Henry. Talk about giving yourself a handicap!

WAY DOWN IN THE BAYEAUX TAPESTRY

Ici Brigette Bardot, avec Jaques Coustea
Jean-Paul George et Ringo, *aw-haw-ee-haw-haw.*
Ils cherchez un bon mot, de Marcel Marceau,
Quesque sais? zero, *aw-haw-ee-haw-haw.*

Madamoiselle d'Anglitaire, dans un petit brassiere,
Avec une joli derriere, *aw-haw-ee-haw-haw.*
Couture de papiere mache, il pleut – quelle horeur;
Nous avons un expose, *aw-haw-ee-haw-haw.*

Je suis Anglais, ma fiancée,
Aime la vie Francais, *aw-haw-ee-haw-haw.*
The kiss – naturelement, the knickers – pour le frisson,
The letter – pour la denoument, *aw-haw-ee-haw-haw.*

J'ai un bette noir – moi je n'aim pas
Eric Cantona, *aw-haw-ee-haw-haw.*
Un autre chose, aussi – beaucoup d'ennui -
La Grande flipping Priz, *aw-haw-ee-haw-haw.*

Josephine et Bonapart dans un menage-a-trois
Avec le Marquis de Sade, *aw-haw-ee-haw-haw.*
Josephine est ooh-la-la, Bonapart est ha-ha-ha,
Le Marquis est come-ci comme-ca, *aw-haw-ee-haw-haw.*

SID KIPPER SAYS: *"When George wanted to write a Cajun song he knew it would have to be in French, and the trouble with that was he don't know much French. So he used what bits he did know. Well, we all know a bit don't we? Things like* cor anglais, *which means French horn. And* condom, *which means French letter. Then there's* haut couture, *which means French dressing. 'Sailor V', that's what I say."*

66

We thought about doing strawberries again that year. Sid said the rooks were nesting high up, and the snails were walking in straight lines. All that nature stuff. He said it meant we'd have a good summer. He was into all that. I said I was going to Sidmouth, so that was that. And all about it.

This birthday business was beginning to get under my skin. Subcutaneous. That's the medical term, so the prison doctor tells me. He also tells me I'm as fit as a flea. That's another medical term, I suppose. It doesn't sound that good to me. Fleas don't live long.

I wasn't really thinking of retiring. Not by a long chalk. But I was considering slowing down a bit. Handing over a few responsibilities. To the boys. Len and Sid. Then I got to thinking about something else. What about all my cash?

I'd never really thought about it before. I'd just collected it. I mean. I knew people made money, and that was a good thing. Apparently. But I wouldn't live for ever. So where would it go then?

It started keeping me awake at nights. So I went poaching with Sid. Shame to waste a perfectly good case of insomnia. But all the time I kept thinking about my money, up in Pit Piece. I'd kept it safe, all these decades. I'd added to it year by year. I'd kept it up to date. But in all that time I'd never really thought about what I wanted it for. A rainy day, I'd assumed. Well there'd been plenty of them. All they did was set me worrying that the money would get flooded. Annie's wedding, I'd thought. Now that looked about as likely as a jolly ballad.

I think Annie loved Sid. I know Sid quite fancied Raquel. But not exclusively. Raquel wanted Sid but felt sorry for Annie, and was not averse to a bit on the side in the meantime. I think Cyril Cockle fancied Annie, but his wife wouldn't wear it. Which was surprising. Given what she actually chose to wear. It was a classic love polygon. Oh yes, I know about polygons. I know they're not missing parrots. I've had a fair bit of education since I've been here. I've done Economics. Woodwork. The Economics of Woodwork. All sorts of stuff. Plus all the books I could read. And not a single page bent.

But I was talking about my money. Well, no, I wasn't talking about it. Because it was secret. But I was thinking about it, as I've told you. And I was coming to the conclusion that it was absolutely useless. It was doing nothing. And over that Spring I realised that I'd simply have to give it all away. I was getting too old for the responsibility. Not to mention all the digging. The only question was who to give it to. Well, obviously that wasn't the only question. There were others. As Uncle Albert used to say, 'The big question is what's the big answer?' It didn't help, really.

Meanwhile, I was getting ready for my Sidmouth trip. I put new strings on the guitar. Even though none of the old ones had broken. I bought some sandals, and had my fancy waistcoat cleaned. I checked the train times and the bus connections. And I borrowed a tent.

Because although I'd been invited to go to Sidmouth it wasn't exactly a booking. I still had to buy a ticket. They'd promised me exposure, but they hadn't offered me accommodation. That's why I borrowed the tent. So finally Annie's camping came in useful. She had all the gear. And I gave Annie a shock. She said I could have the gear if I made a small donation to the Brownies. I don't think she expected much. I had a reputation for tight dealing. So she very nearly fainted when I handed over £500, only slightly muddy. It was the start of a new way for me. It felt good. I hadn't been able to get a reaction out of Annie for decades.

I would go to Sidmouth, and join in with all those enthusiastic young people. I wouldn't even mind if they kept their clothes on. I would immerse myself in the music. The songs. The dance. My life would never be the same again.

Sadly, only the last bit came true.

DEADLY DICK'S

Oh me name is Dick O' - Real - ly, I was lead - er of the band; There was
Mick who mauled the lute, Ric the fid - dle flay - er, and There was
Nick who tort - ured flutes, but the star, there's no dis - pute, Was my -
- self, bec - ause I beat the day - lights out of my bod - hran. And we played
'Dead - ly, dead - ly, dead - ly, dead - ly, dead - ly, dead - ly, die!

SID KIPPER *SAYS: "This is all about when they tried to revive the old Icenic 'deadly' music. It was supposed to be played to strike fear into the hearts of the enemy. I believe the Celts have something similar."*

"The best-laid plans of Meissen men", as they say in Germany. "It all went pair shaped", as they say in Antingham. "Everything went pips up." I don't know where they say that. Maybe in Sidmouth. I never did get there to find out. Now maybe I never will.

I blame Mrs Thatcher. Because it was that tax rebate that finished me. I'd forgotten clean about it, what with all the excitement. Then Len, who looked after such things, said "You've got a cheque." Well, that was a turnup for the books. I'd never had one before. Oh, sometimes people paid that way. But I got them to make it out to Len, and he turned it into cash. I never asked how. But now there was this cheque. Made out to "George Kipper – account payee only". I was angry at first. How dare they call me an account payee only? But Len explained that it meant the cheque could only be paid into my account. He said I'd have to open an account and pay the cheque in. Then I could get my money.

Well, what with Sidmouth, and my new life, and so on, I completely forgot the oath I'd sworn. All those years ago. I caught the bus to North Walsham, and headed for Gurnards Bank. The nearer I got, the stranger I felt. It went against the grain. I turned up my collar and pulled down my hat. So as not to be recognised. The sun-glasses helped as well. I glanced around me. In court they said I did it furtively. At the time I was just checking that nobody I knew saw me. I don't know why, really. I held firmly on to my collapsible umbrella. In my pocket. I don't know why I did that, either.

When I went into the bank it was terrible. It was all designed to make you feel small. There were even people in suits. I edged up to a counter. I reached in my pocket for the cheque. And it wasn't there. I think I was relieved, to tell the truth. I turned on my heels and fled. I could only think of getting back to St Just, where I knew what was going on.

I was sort of aware of some bother at the other entrance to the bank. I heard some shouting. Then the squeal of tyres. But I could only think of getting a fast bus out of there. Wishful thinking, of course. I had to settle for a slow one as usual.

Oh me name is Dick O'Really, I was leader of the band;
There was Mick who mauled the lute, Ric the fiddle flayer, and
There was Nick who tortured flutes, but the star, there's no dispute,
Was myself, because I beat the daylights out of my bodhran.
  And we played 'Deadly, deadly, deadly, deadly, deadly, deadly, die!'

Well the band all got together in the back room of the Star,
Where we thrashed the deadly tune for hours and hours and hours and hours.
We slaughtered Paddy Doyle, then a Sailor's Life we spoiled,
And decided that we'd call ourselves Four Deadbeats In The Bar.

When we picked up a tune it soon became a strain,
Then we executed it without any refrain.
Every jig and every reel we squeezed until they squealed,
It's a wonder they survived until we thrashed them once again.

If the truth be told not everybody found the music fun;
In fact, beside ourselves, that is, there wasn't even one!
Hugh the Vicar sat and prayed, his turned off hearing aid,
And Fred said if he had one he'd go home and fetch his gun.

We tried to play for dancing, and it should have been great but
The dancers went and spoilt it and the reason's quite clear-cut;
When we went free-for-all at Phil the Fluter's Ball,
As we doubled up the speed the buggers just would not keep up.

Well at closing time the landlord asked us why we played that stuff;
"For the kicks and for the crack," was the way Nick summed it up.
So first he cracked Nick's flute, kicked the fiddle through the lute,
And shoved my bodhran where I'd have to play it standing up!
Well at the time I cried, but now I feel such pride,
For I can say that I was there the day the deadly died.

When I got home I found the cheque straight away. Propped up on the mantelpiece. And once again I swore to have nothing to do with banks. That cheque could jolly well go up to Pit Piece with all the other money. I'd bury it that night.

I was in quite a state after my experience at the bank. I may not have been quite as careful as I might. Or I might not have been quite as careful as I may. Whichever it was I got to Pit Piece, and straight away began to dig. Before long I had my money exposed. Then I got the cheque out of my pocket. And that was the moment when all hell broke loose. It was worse than Deadly music. Almost.

Whistles blew. Lights flashed. Dogs barked. And through it all I heard Sergeant Sturgeon bellow "I've got you at last, Mister George Kipper." Well I knew at once I was in serious trouble. He'd never called me Mister before. I thought it was jolly unfair. I mean. I didn't even know it was illegal to bury a cheque. And while I was thinking all that I was also running for dear life. It was instinct. It was self-preservation.

The warden has just told me that's the latest thing in GM crops. Self-preservation. No more need for jam-making, apparently. I hope Dot hears about it soon.

I fled from Pit Piece. I got away easily enough. Years of poaching meant I had no trouble evading them on my own ground. But I couldn't stay on my own ground. I couldn't go home. Because they knew where I lived. I had to get away. Maybe I could hide up somewhere.

But that's enough. It's not a pleasant story. And it doesn't have a happy ending.

EXCUSE ME

Well I heard that this pub had some mus-ic, I heard that they
had tunes and songs, So I got my-self there nice and ear-ly,
And I soon found I had-n't heard wrong. There were fid-dles, mouth
org-ans and ban-jos; Mel-od-i-ans, bones and guit-ars,
And they squeezed and they plucked, they blew and they sucked, Play-ing dan-ces from
ne-ar and far. They played pol-kas and horn-pipes and walt-zes,
As if they'd gone in-to a trance. But though they played
dan-ces the whole long night through, Not one cou-ple got up to dance.

SIDKIPPER SAYS: *"Reedham Ferry is the only way across the River Yare between Norwich and Yarmouth, which is twenty miles. Unless you think Yarmouth is in the Isle of Wight, of course, in which case it's a hell of a lot further, but you wouldn't go that way, anyway.*

For another thing, it's also the place where my Uncle George finally got caught. He'd been on the run three days, pursued by the constabulary. He was riding a monocycle, disguised as a French onion seller. Well, it was a bicycle when he nicked it from outside Ranworth Village Hall while everyone was distracted by barn dancing. But the front wheel had dropped off in Halvergate during the chase, so now it was a monocycle. And he couldn't actually get hold of any onions at short notice, so he was wearing a string of sugar beet round his neck instead. Which was not so daft, because he was headed for Cantley, where he was going to hide up at the sugar-beet factory. He'd worked there once. Once was enough, he always reckoned.

So there he was, with his sugar beet round his neck, whistling 'Froggie Went A-Wooing-Oh' to keep up his disguise, and pedalling like hell, because he was being hotly pursued by Sergeant Sturgeon, on a motorised lawn-mower. He'd had a double puncture on his police tandem in Freethorpe.

Well I heard that this pub had some music, I heard that they had tunes and songs,
So I got myself there nice and early, and I soon found I hadn't heard wrong.
There were fiddles, mouth-organs and banjos; melodeons, bones and guitars,
And they squeezed and they plucked, they blew and they sucked,
                              playing dances from near and far.
    They played polkas and hornpipes and waltzes, as if they'd gone into a trance.
    But though they played dances the whole long night through, not one couple got up to dance.

The arrival of drinks stopped the music, so I went straight into a song,
But before I had reached the first chorus the whole lot were playing along.
It started off as a slow ballad, but they played it diddle-de-dee;
Well, I wouldn't have minded them speeding it up if they'd been in the same key as me!

Now a lady had taken my fancy, so I thought that I'd take my chance,
And as she was tapping her toe to the tune I went over and asked her to dance.
She didn't say no straight away; then she looked at me and laughed,
And she carried on reading her paper as if I was the one that was daft.

By now I was getting frustrated, but I'm not the sort just to moan;
I thought it was time that I took a stand, so I stood up and danced on my own.
Then came a tap on the shoulder – had I found my partner at last?
But the landlady's son said "Excuse me", and I left with his boot up my arse.

So I set off hot foot for the barn dance, some serious dancing I planned;
I knew from the poster I'd have a good time with the old Push And Pull ceilidh band.
They finished a dance as I entered; I thought, "That's good timing", but wrong!
Just then some weird people got up on the stage and started to sing some old songs.
They sang ballads and carols and shanties, and choruses no one joined in,
And as they droned on, for song after song, I thought "Well, you can't bloody win!"

Then George had this idea. He reckoned that if he diverted to Reedham Ferry he could cross over, immobilise the ferry on the opposite bank, and leave Sturgeon stranded on the other side of the Yare. Then he could go and get lost in Bungay. He knew he could get lost in Bungay, because he'd been advised to do exactly that every time he'd ever been there. All Norfolk people have. It's what they call being Suffolkated.

But his luck was out. By a terrible stroke of bad fortune he found someone else had had exactly the same idea. So they'd already immobilised the ferry on the other bank, and George was left trapped. Well, that led to a dramatic stand off. They still talk of it today. Well, I haven't actually checked today, but they did last August. George threw lumps of sugar beet at Sturgeon, and Sturgeon minced them up with the lawn mower, and that went on for some time. It was stale, mate. But in the end, as darkness was falling, it was a fair cop. And the fair cop in question was WPC Wendy Whelk, who'd been on the back of the tandem before they had the punctures, and eventually caught up on a space hopper she'd commandeered. Well, quick as a flush she surrounded George, and before you could say 'Jack Russell' he'd been arrested. And that was that for George. He was remanded in custard, tried, found guilty, and sentenced to life, Jim, but not as we know it. Then he went straight to jail, without passing 'Go' or collecting £200. And in those days £200 _was_ £200. Even if you didn't collect it.

And the rest, as they say, is his story."

GREY IS THE COLOUR

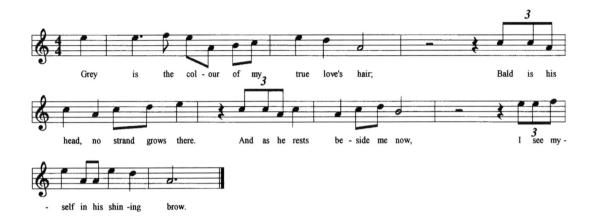

Grey is the colour of my true love's hair;
Bald is his head, no strand grows there.
And as he rests beside me now,
I see myself in his shining brow.

Yellow's the colour of my true love's teeth;
One set above, and one beneath.
And as he dreams his smile I spy –
All in a glass at his bedside.

Red is the colour of my true love's nose;
Likewise his cheeks, his eyes also.
Sleeps like a baby in my bed;
And so he should, for he's bottle fed.

Black is the colour of my true love's nails;
But no one's perfect – all are frail.
One thing alone sets him apart –
Black is the colour of my true love's heart.

Blue is the colour of my true love's lips;
And now his toes, now fingertips.
Soon he'll have all the rest he needs –
I put white arsenic in his morning tea.

SID KIPPER *SAYS: "This is one of George's songs he wrote about fellow inmates. He's done any number of them. Songs like 'For He's A Jolly Good Felon', 'Sammy's Bars' and 'Lock Around The Clock'. This one was originally about a bloke, but George didn't think he'd get any sympathy for that."*

It was a third-class carriage of justice. I was stitched up like a Kipper. I was charged with bank robbery and actual bodily harm. I said I didn't do it. They said I did. I was outvoted.

I don't think my lawyer helped much. Mr Freeman. From Freeman, Hardy and Willis. He was the most respected lawyer in Cromer. Trouble was, the trial was held in Norwich. So it didn't last long. Was I there? Yes. Proof? Yes: I'd dropped my umbrella as I fled. I'd told Ruby. I said that a monogrammed umbrella was asking for trouble. But she'd ignored me as usual. Had I knocked over a little old lady in my rush? Yes. I admitted that. Was I found burying a load of money? Yes. Had I avoided arrest in a manner liable to arouse suspicion? Yes. Was I guilty? As hell.

I told them I didn't do it. I said I could explain everything. But when I did they just laughed out loud. Well, no. Not out loud. That's not a legal sort of thing to do. So they smirked out loud instead. It was all over the papers. There was a special supplement in the *North Norfolk News and Agitator*. 'LOCK UP THIS EVIL SWINE AND THROW AWAY THE KEY' was the headline. They got a lot of complaints. From pig lovers.

So then it came to the sentencing. Bigots Against Tolerance demonstrated outside the court demanding the return of the death penalty for dropping litter. I suppose they meant my umbrella. The judge looked stern. "George Kipper," he said; "You have been found guilty of a heinous crime. You have refused to accept your guilt and shown not one iota of remorse. Therefore you must go to prison for a very long time." He named a figure. I tried to dicker. He was having none of it. He certainly hadn't overstated it. It was a very long time. Too long to contemplate. Let's just say that I wouldn't even come up for parole for nearly twenty years. But I'll be coming back to that.

I was driven off in a prison van to a holding area at Norwich Jail. It wasn't very nice. You didn't meet a very good class of people there. Many of them were criminals. Don't get me wrong. I'm the last person to judge my fellow man. Or woman. Although I'm not sure you can call a woman a fellow. But at the time it was a shock. Because I hadn't done anything illegal. Well, that's not strictly true. I'd done lots of illegal things. But not the one I got jailed for. It was a bitter pils to swallow. And I never liked lager very much in the first place.

Eventually I was transferred to where I am now. The Isle of Wight. I'd said I wanted to be somewhere near Yarmouth. I reckon it was done to spite me. The warden says that come August they'll have a do to celebrate my twenty years here. There'll be a cake. But it won't have a file in it.

Back then I was the new boy. There was talk of an initiation, but I wasn't frightened. I'd used the lavatories at the Goat Inn. Nothing could be worse than that. In the end it never happened. Or, if it did, I wasn't there at the time.

I soon settled down to the routine. Get up. Slop out. Exercise. Work. Dinner. Work. Recreation. Supper. Lock up. Lights out. Just like being at home, really. Only without the nagging. Of course, there were things I missed. A pint. Another pint. That sort of thing. But I soon found you could get most things. If you knew how. And who. There was any amount of wheeling and dealing. I was soon back in business. Just like at home. Except I had to spend the money.

The thing that really rankled was nothing to do with where I was. It was all to do with where I hadn't been. Sidmouth International Festival. Because the robbery, the chase and everything happened just before I was supposed to go there. That's why I'd gone to the bank. To make sure that damned cheque was safe while I was away. But even that wasn't the worst of it. Not by half.

You see, Sid and Henry went to Sidmouth in my stead. Called themselves 'The Kipper Family'. Sang all the old songs, and became an overnight success. They got bookings. A record deal. The lot.

And that should have been me

MAN OF CONVICTIONS

I was first led ast-ray in the pub one night when These long-haired blokes start-ed to sing A-bout mag-ic drag-ons and tam-bour-ine men, And oth-er pe-cu-li-ar things. So I smoked this fag, which didn't half make me cough, They said it would soon set me free; But when I knocked Con-sta-ble John's hel-met off It did quite the op-po-site for me. I'm a man of con-vict-ions, but I was con-fined; I got one night's rest-rict-ion for step-ping out of line. Then came the in-flict-ion of a twen-ty pound fine; In that jing-le, jang-le morn-ing I'll come fol-low-ing you.

The next few years were sheer hell. Not because I was locked up. I could deal with that. Because of Henry and Sid's success. They made radio programmes. People listened to them. They recorded albums. People bought them. They even had the nerve to record some of my songs. 'The Village P.I.M.P.' 'Joan Sugarbeet'. Others. Then they put some of my songs in a book. Worse yet, they signed over all the rights to someone else. I bet Henry made the deal! I trained Sid better than that.

They did a record called 'The Ever Decreasing Circle'. On the sleeve Sid said he was running a 'George Kipper Is Innocent' campaign. And he did try. He even got into court at one stage, where he questioned the evidence. Idiot. He should have questioned the witnesses. I suppose he was advised by Mr Freeman. The man with the inappropriate name.

To be fair, though, I don't feel so inclined, they did get me on to a couple of albums. It was when I was home. On passionate leave. That's the hardest part of being in prison. Which is one half of a dirty joke. If you can work out the other half don't blame me. It's your mind.

Being on an album is alright. But just doing backing vocals is more like an insult. And as they toured the country, making millions, I was locked up, making mail-bags. While they were having their every whim supplied by willing groupies, I was having my every whim denied by willing wardens. And while they topped the bill at the Trunch Village Pimp Festival, I was questioned by the Bill about "Other Matters That Have Come To Our Attention". At least nothing came of that. Thank goodness.

It's just as well I'm not a bitter man.

I was first led astray in the pub one night when
These long-haired blokes started to sing
About magic dragons and tambourine men,
And other peculiar things.
So I smoked this fag, which didn't half make me cough,
They said it would soon set me free;
But when I knocked Constable John's helmet off
It did quite the opposite for me.
    I'm a man of convictions, but I was confined;
    I got one night's restriction for stepping out of line.
    Then came the infliction of a twenty-pound fine;
    In that jingle, jangle morning I'll come following you.

When I next heard them sing 'twas the landlords they scoffed,
They sang "This land is my land and yours."
So I went out next morning, and fenced a bit off,
And used it for grazing my horse.
But then Colonel Heart said the land was his own,
And forced me to take down the fence.
Well the Lord forgives trespass, but the magistrates don't,
And Heart was the chair of the bench.
    I'm a man of convictions, I told them with pride,
    And your jurisdiction I hereby deny;
    Impressed with my diction they gave me three months inside,
    But the times, they are a changin'.

When I'd finished my sentence I swore I'd be deaf
To the songs they were singing to me.
But when they sang one about how property's theft,
I jumped up and cried, "Glory be!"
For now I could see that the reason I'm poor
Is because someone else has stolen it all,
So I stole it back, plus a little bit more,
And here's what I said at the trial:
    I'm a man of convictions, it can't be denied,
    It's just contradiction that caused me to slide.
    But they said that's fiction, take two years inside,
    But you know that was the last thing on my mind.

Now older, but wiser, I came out today,
And I went for a nice quiet drink,
But those blasted folk-singers they started again,
And once again set me to think.
They sang that for freedom of speech they'd a lust,
And how for that freedom they'd fight;
They swore to that end they would die if they must,
So I just helped them prove they were right.
    I'm a man of convictions, I don't think I did wrong,
    By means of constriction I ended their song,
    My lawyer's prediction is bleak from hereon,
    But we shall overcome, some day.

SID KIPPER SAYS: *"If you read my previous comment, then this is another one. If you didn't it still is, but you won't know what I'm on about."*

WE'RE NORFOLK AND GOOD

In praise of my coun-ty I'm go-ing to sing; A-gainst this fine place I will not hear a thing. If you speak ill a-bout it you speak a false-hood, For my na-tive coun-ty is Nor-folk and good. Nor-folk and good, Nor-folk and good: We are the boys who are Nor-folk and good.

SID KIPPER SAYS: *"You have to be careful how you sing this song, otherwise people might think you were singing something rude. And there's enough of that in folk-singing already."*

After I got this job in the prison library I settled back to make the most of it. I told myself I'd been thinking of taking it a bit easier. Anyway. I'd always wanted more time to write songs. I continued. This was an opportunity. I concluded. Sometimes I almost believed me.

Life in prison is different to life outside. You have to learn to talk. When you're not supposed to. So you learn to chop. Sentences. Up into. Little bits. Once you've. Done that. It's hard. To stop. Some. Times.

It was true, though. I did have plenty of time for song-writing. Quite a few of the ones in this book have been written since I came here. In 1989 I wrote one of my biggest hits ever. It was for when my little village was Norfolk Village Of Culture. 'We're Norfolk And Good' it was called. It was based on what Uncle Albert used to call 'a play on worms'. It was a great success. They tell me that children could be heard singing it on the way to school. They reckon they got a good telling off for it, too.

Which is a good thing, if you ask me. If not, don't bother. I'll ask myself. Children nowadays have it far too easy. They don't have the discipline we had in my day. They've even done away with my favourite calendar custom. Children In Need Of A Clip Round The Ear Day. As for the old New Year tradition of child baiting, well! Now the little dears mustn't suffer physically. Now it has to be just psychological. So all they do these days is for the shops to put notices in their windows for the children to see. 'Back To School'. I gather it works pretty well.

Of course in my day we had to be seen, and not herd. Kids now wouldn't believe it. If more than three or four of us got together they used to break us up. With sticks. Or dogs. Whichever came to hand. That way you never got mobs. Well, life was hard, as I may have mentioned. If you wanted an apple you had to scrump it yourself. And if you got caught you had to take the punishment. And that used to fit the crime, what's more. If you've ever spent a day tying windfalls back on the tree with bits of string you'll know what I mean. If not, I'm probably wasting my time writing this. But that doesn't matter, really. I've got to waste my time somehow.

So I might as well waste it on the likes of you.

In praise of my county I'm going to sing;
Against this fine place I will not hear a thing.
If you speak ill about it you speak a falsehood,
For my native county is Norfolk and good.
    Norfolk and good, Norfolk and good:
    We are the boys who are Norfolk and good.

Now Nelson from Norfolk he took on the world,
Lady Hamilton thought him an absolute pearl.
But Hardy said Nelson was misunderstood;
He reckoned his kissing was Norfolk and good.

Now England for actors has won great renown,
But when they talk Norfolk they all let us down.
To larn to talk proper they could, if they would,
But since they will not they are Norfolk and good.

Now Kent has its cobs, and the Cornish their pasties,
And Lancashire hot-pot can be awfully tasty.
In Cheshire there's cheese and in Yorkshire there's pud,
But my wife's old dumplings are Norfolk and good.

Now the rich folk from London our county have found,
Which means all our houses cost thousands of pounds.
They all feel at home in our neighbourhood,
So we let them know that they're Norfolk and good.

Now our Norfolk turkeys are simply the best,
They sure knock the stuffing out of the rest.
And if you tried one I'm sure that you would
Agree that our turkeys are Norfolk and good.

The warden has been on holiday again. To St Just. He tells me everyone is well and they send their best wishes. I asked where he'd stayed. I was just making small talk. But for some reason he got a bit leery. Said he couldn't quite remember, and changed the subject. I assume he stayed at the Old Goat. That's something you'd want to forget if you could.

It made me a bit homesick. I thought of the pleasant evenings I'd had in the Old Goat. Both of them. Then I remembered all the other evenings. That made me feel better. Then, in my mind, I saw my Ruby. In her pomp. Behind the bar. She was a fine figure of a woman in those days. People chose to use the Goat just because of Ruby. And just because it was the only pub in the village, I suppose. Ernie Spratt used to say, "Ruby's two greatest assets are the pub's greatest asset." Not like the Crown, in Trunch. In those days the barmaid in the Crown was pretty skinny. Mind you, the beer was a lot better. Or so they say. I've never been there because the Kipper family have been barred from the Crown for generations. It's traditional. Which is another reason Len was so disappointing, all those years ago.

Now I hear that Sid has been in the Crown. I asked him what about standards? What about tradition? He said I was out of touch. Things move on. And what if they close the Goat one day? Where would he go then? I said he had a point. But not a good one.

Ruby came to visit last month. I couldn't help thinking that if they were still the Goat's greatest asset Sid would have a point. But she doesn't do the barmaiding any more. She does the food now. Mainly to stop Dot doing it. It's a public service.

DAISIES UP

When he is born a-a man has no hair, Then it starts sprout-ing out ever-y-where; When he get old then his hair all drops out; Some-times I won-der what life's al-ll a--bout! What is the life of a man an-y more than a leaf? His veins all stand out, he gets spots und-er-neath. A leaf may not stum-ble, or drib-ble, or cough, But just like an old man it al-ways dro-ops off.

SIDKIPPER SAYS: *"George wrote this one for my old father, Henry, when he retired from the folk singing business. Some people were fooled into thinking it was 'the real thing', but it wasn't. It was just my old father."*

In early 1991 I had a visit from Sid. He comes to see me now and then. I think I already told you that. So don't say I never tell you anything.

But this was a special visit. He said he had a problem. I said I knew that. He sang with him. My brother Henry had always been a problem. In that case, said Sid, he had a problem with his problem. He said Henry was getting worse. He was forgetting his words on stage. Even when they were written down in front of him. In large print. What could Sid do?

I said he should go solo and wait till I was available again. Ah, he said. But how was he going to persuade Henry to retire? I told him.

We set up a surprise retirement party for Henry. Only it wouldn't just be the party that was a surprise. The whole thing would be what they call a *fate accomplished*. All the plans were laid in secret. I wrote a special song and arranged passionate leave. And when it finally happened the whole thing was recorded for a gramophone record. 'In The Family Way'. I even got to sing the lead on one track. But it wasn't just a record. It was a permanent record. Because that way Henry couldn't go back on it.

It all worked a treat. Immediately after the party Henry was whisked off on a farewell tour to cash in. And I was whisked back here to slop out.

When he is born a man has no hair,
Then it starts sprouting out everywhere;
When he gets old then his hair all drops out;
Sometimes I wonder what life's all about!
What is the life of a man any more than a leaf?
His veins all stand out, he gets spots underneath.
A leaf may not stumble, or dribble, or cough,
But just like an old man it always drops off.

When he is young a man's always busy,
Courting his Fancy, or Nancy, or Lizzie.
When he is old he has time for repose;
He slips on his slippers, and lands on his nose.
What is the life of a man any more than a frog?
They both spend a lot of their time in the bog.
Even though in this world we appear dark and glum,
Like a frog we must hop it when our time has come.

When a man's in his prime he'll labour all day,
To find any reason his work to delay.
When he grows old then his body's no use;
At least then he needn't invent an excuse.
What is the life of a man any more than a cow?
He'll spend all his lifetime yoked to the plough.
He must work like a slave, though he'd much rather chuck it;
Like a cow he'll be milked, and then kick the bucket.

In later years a man starts to regret
The chances he's missed and the maids he's not met.
He tries to catch up with these maids while he can,
And so he becomes a dirty old man.
What is the life of a man any more than a bird?
He feathers his nest till at last he's interred.
Though he sings and he soars, as if there's no stopping,
When he falls he is just like another bird dropping.

Now I am old and not long for this life,
I must soon bid adieu to my loved ones – and wife.
Even though in this world things appear dark and glum,
The Parson assures me there's worse yet to come.
What is the life of a man any more than a mole?
He spends all his time in the dark, on the whole.
Though for a while he may pick buttercups,
Like a mole in a hole, he will push daisies up.

EAST SIDE STORY

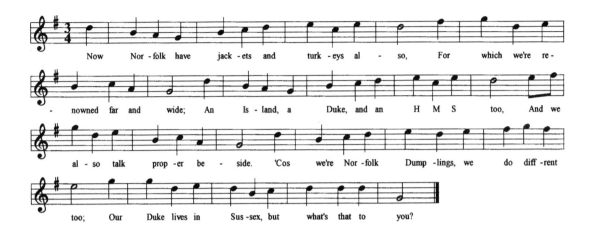

Now Nor-folk have jack-ets and turk-eys al-so, For which we're re-nowned far and wide; An Is-land, a Duke, and an H M S too, And we al-so talk prop-er be-side. 'Cos we're Nor-folk Dump-lings, we do diff-rent too; Our Duke lives in Sus-sex, but what's that to you?

SID KIPPER SAYS: *"People from Norfolk are known as 'Norfolk Dumplings'. Some of them get carried away about being Norfolk. Well, Bigots Against Tolerance do. Their latest thing is to send people back where they come from. The rule is 'first in, first out'. So people in Norfolk with Roman noses should look out."*

Yesterday the warden asked me what I thought was the worst time to be here. That was easy. I said it was now. But that was only partly true. Because the worst worst time to be here is when now happens to fall on Christmas Day. On Christmas Day this place is very quiet. Because people are thinking of home.

I can remember Christmasses years ago. When the children were young. All the invitations. To go outside for a fight. The Cockles' fancy-dress party. Where you had to come as a scarecrow. It had to be held outdoors. Because it's hard to get indoors with a broomstick stuck through both sleeves.

Then we used to go round village carol-singing. And people used to put something in collecting bucket. Sometimes it was money!

And on December 21st there was a big do at Henry's house. There were balloons. And inside catering. Everything. I don't know if December 21st is big with you? Probably not. It's probably not your sister-in-law's birthday.

I remember it all. I remember the Trunch Victorian Fayre. When the whole village went Victorian, and we had loads of period fun. First thing in the morning they used to call on all the poor people. And drag them off to the workhouse. Then all the little boys were sent up chimneys. And the little girls had to stand shivering on the street corner selling lucky heather. Marvellous. And it was all sponsored by The Gruel Marketing Board. Mind you. It wasn't quite as old and traditional as they liked to make out. There's no record of the Victorian Fayre before 1838.

Of course it's all gone mad now. People get huge presents. They're spoiled. I tell you. When I was a boy we were glad if we got rickets for Christmas. In some families even one ricket was a treat. And I don't think people are any happier now than we were. A good deal cleaner. But no happier.

Now Norfolk have jackets and turkeys also,
For which we're renowned far and wide;
An Island, a Duke, and an HMS too,
And we also talk proper beside.
'Cos we're Norfolk Dumplings, we do different too;
Our Duke lives in Sussex, but what's that to you?

When we have a 'do' then the grass is all wet,
A 'thud''s one divided by three;
We stand in a 'coup' when we've something to get,
And 'hare''s where we happen to be.
'Cos we're Norfolk Dumplings, we do different here;
Abroad's what we sail on, but what do we care?

When them others say 'boles' they mean bowls in fact;
And when they say 'bowels' they mean bum.
So out in the shires where they talk strange like that,
A bowls match must be something rum!
'Cos we're Norfolk Dumplings, we do different too;
Our greens are uncrowned, and we do have a clue.

Now in Sweden and Suffolk and such foreign parts
They've their own ways of getting along.
Well we don't tell them how to do what they do,
We just point out they're doing it wrong.
'Cos we're Norfolk Dumplings, we do different here;
Our Line goes all over, and we hate frothy beer.

In Gimingham, Trimingham, Knapton and Trunch,
In Northrepps, and Southrepps, and Cley.
We say what we like, and we like what we say,
And I hope you'll all go do likewise.
'Cos we're Norfolk Dumplings, we do different too;
I may be due to do more, but, do not, that'll do!

Because possessions bring problems. Don't they. I wrote a little song about it:

Shut up little baby, hold your row,
Daddy's gonna buy you a clockwork cow;
And if that clockwork cow should break,
Back to the shop Daddy it will take;
And if that shop won't replace it,
Daddy's gonna give them a big fat lip;
And if that big fat lip should yell,
Daddy's gonna get out of there pell mell,
And if Daddy should trip and falls down a quarry,
That'll serve you right and then you'll be sorry.

I think that says it all. Mind you. There's plenty in here who aren't so sentimental. Some of them didn't really have homes. Some of them are desperate characters. Like 'Slasher' Jenkins. Everyone calls him A11. Because he's dangerous when crossed. Or 'Razor' Ruddock. He suffered from abuse as a boy. Mind you, I think it was mostly self abuse. And, of course. Most of them in here are as thick as two short thieves.

But just because they've committed terrible crimes. Where their victims suffered horribly. That doesn't make them bad people. Does it?

THE DRAG HUNT

Said old Per-cy Jen-kins, "Come, come me brave boys, Be up-stand-ing and toss off your drink; We won't let those spo-il sports kill all our joy, So we'll take to the fields dressed in pink. With high hee-led shoes, and mat-ching hand-bags, We will do as we please and go hunt-ing in drag".

On Christmas Day we listened to Trunch Wireless. They did 'Nine Lessons and Carols'. And they were proper old-fashioned lessons, too. Done by Mrs Fry. Who used to be the Headmistress. She used to line up nine children, ceremonially clip their ears, and say "Let that be a lesson to you!" Then we had all the old carols. Like 'As With Gladys':

As with Gladys men of old did the facts of life behold;
As with Joy they spent the night, leading onward, beaming bright;
Now to such delights may we, Evelyn, be led by thee.

But that was all just to take our minds off Christmas dinner. Because we used to go to Henry's for that. Even when we weren't talking. Well, you know what they say. Blood is thicker than water. But custard is thicker than both. So Dot used to do the works. Turkey. Stuffing. Vegetables. Right through to the Christmas pudding. Now. The secret of Christmas pudding is in the steaming. Dot always borrowed a two-pudding, double-D hammock-steamer from Ruby. It's one reason why Ruby was always a bit wobbly around Christmas. Dot steamed the puddings for several weeks. Then, come the moment, she tipped them out. And decorated each one with a glacé cherry. It looked marvellous. Which was all very well if you only had to look at them.

On Boxing Day we went out. Everybody does. To get away from their relations. I suppose. Round our way it was a day for fox-hunting. And morris dancing.

I don't know where you stand on fox-hunting. I can guess where you stand on morris dancing. For fox-hunting, I'm like Sid. I sit on the fence. Well, I did when I was living at home. If I sat on the fence around here they might not be best pleased. They tell me there's a new law coming in about hunting. I looked it up. It shouldn't be a problem. It's going to ban "hunting wild mammals with dogs". Well, that's alright. They don't use dogs, do they? They use hounds. Fox hounds for foxes. Otter hounds for otters. Grey hounds for old people. And blood hounds for close relatives.

I've thought of some other ways round it. Well, I've had the time. They could leave the dogs at home and just use the bitches. Or they could tame the mammals first. Or they could go back to what they did in the old days. At the end of the season, when everything else had been hunted or poached, or otherwise died of unnatural causes, they often used to have a magnificent beetle drive!

But I think I may have found the best way of all. I won't spell it out. Because I don't want to give it away. But I've put it in a song. As a word to the wise. The stupid will have to look after themselves.

Said old Percy Jenkins, "Come, come me brave boys,
Be upstanding and toss off your drink;
We won't let those spoil sports kill all our joy,
So we'll take to the fields dressed in pink.
With high heeled shoes, and matching handbags,
We will do as we please and go hunting in drag."

So Saul became Sal, and Bill became Bliss,
And Monty became Montreal.
Each he was a she, and each master a miss,
Although they were new to it all.
So it's p'raps not surprising that Nan (who was Ned),
Rode round in rings with his tights on his head.

Now Pet (who was Peter) had sought
To get into Alice's pants.
Well now he succeeded, but ruefully thought
That this wasn't quite what he'd meant.
And Alice was left, a touch ill at ease,
Just viewing the chase and feeling the breeze.

Said Len (who was Liza), "Some dogs must be found,
To help us to track Reynard's trail;
But let us not hunt with those big noisy hounds,
For their colours would clash with my nails."
So as they went hunting their dogs they were these:
Three poodles, a chihuahua, and two pekinese.

Soon the dogs had bold Reynard up and away,
With Fifi and Fluff on his trail;
And after a chase they had him at bay,
Where they licked him, and all wagged their tails.
The fox turned to face them, just catching his breath;
Saw the dogs, saw the hunters, and laughed himself to death!

Now no one on earth their sport can prevent,
They'll take to the field without fear;
And soon, once again, they will pick up the scent,
And dab it behind both their ears.
They'll ride, side by side, over dale and hill,
With pride in their breasts, and all dressed to kill.

SID KIPPER SAYS: *"Some people are always wanting to ban things, like fox-hunting, and the bomb, and joes. Although I suppose that last lot have got a point. But if anyone tries to stop them doing something they go on about their humane rights. Well they can't have it both ways! So how come they always do?"*

PRETTY PENNY-OH

As I went dow, as he went dow, As we went down to Limp-en-hoe, The cap-tain he was hot for a la-dy, like as not, And the name that she had was Pret-ty Pen-ny-oh.

from DOT KIPPER'S BOOK OF HANDY CHRISTMAS HINTS

ROASTED TURKEY

This here is a good way of dealing with problem turkeys.

INGREDIENTS: One turkey (or more if you've got an infestation).

METHOD: Put it in the oven, and roast it. Serve with crammed berry sauce and gibbet gravy.

TIP: A turkey always takes longer to cook than you think. Which means that even if you know that, and allow extra time, it'll still be half raw when you want to serve it up.

HORSE CHESTNUT STUFFING

You need stuffing at Christmas, just like crackers, leg and breast. Otherwise nobody would have nothing to make smutty jokes about.

INGREDIENTS: One horse, and one chestnut.

METHOD: Mix thoroughly, and use to stuff the bird.

TIP: Be careful not to stuff the horse and then try to mix thoroughly with the turkey.

CHRISTMAS TEA

The most important part of Christmas tea is the tea itself. Now, a lot of people nowadays don't make tea proper. They seem to think it's all about sticking a bag in a mug (as opposed to the Cockles' love life, which Claude's mother reckons is all about sticking a mug in a bag). But making tea proper is simple enough if you know how. If not, it's nigh on impossible.

INGREDIENTS: Tea, and water.

METHOD: First off, bring a kettle of freshly drawed water to a rolling boil, and use some of that to warm up the pot, making sure you swish it all round. Then warm the spout by tipping the water out of the pot through it. Now, go over to the dresser and fetch the tea caddy. Come back with that, open it up, and carefully measure out one level teaspoon of tea per person, plus one level teaspoon for the pot, in the pot (use a spirit level if you're not sure). Put the tea in the pot, and replace the caddy. Now carry the pot over to the stove, and take the kettle off the heat. Actually, hold you hard a minute. I forgot to tell you to put the kettle back on the heat after the pot-warming, so if you haven't, do that now. Of course, in that case you may need to go back and warm the pot again. Which would mean tipping the tea out first. Anyhow, when you've done all that, pour the boiling water into the teapot. Now put the kettle to one side, and put the lid back on the pot (I left it to your common sense to take the lid off. If you didn't you'll be too busy mopping up and putting dressings on the scalds to read this, so we'll carry on without you). Now cover the pot up with the tea-cosy, and let it stand so the tea can draw.

Meanwhile get out cups, saucers, teaspoons, sugar and milk. Plus minced pies and turkey sand-wedges, of course, which you prepared earlier. Then, when the tea is ready, put the milk into the cups first, and then draw the pot towards you and pour the tea. Add sugar to taste, or lack of it, and stick your little finger stuck out. After that you're on your own.

TIP: You'll know if the tea is stewed, because then it'll draw your bum and elbows together.

As I went dow, as he went dow,
As we went down to Limpenhoe,
The captain he was hot for a lady, like as not,
And the name that she had was Pretty Penny-oh.

She was a broad, she was a broad,
She was a broad hearted lass-ee-o;
She'd a bright and sparkling eye, and here's the reason why –
It was made from the very finest glass-ee-o.

He's shinning up the lad, he's shinning up the lad,
He's shinning up the ladder to her window-oh;
Through the window he did slide, but there was no light inside,
So his foot slipped off into the pot below.

He found her bra, he found her bra,
He found her brass bedstead-ee-oh.
So though it was pitch black he located her by that,
Though he tripped on the cat and banged his head-ee-oh.

"No longer wee, no longer wee,
No longer weep for your love-ee-oh."
Then oh so very neat he slipped between the sheets,
And burned himself on her hot-water bottlee-oh.

She soon discerned his sigh, she soon discerned his sigh,
She soon discerned his sighs as he lay by her-oh;
Let there be no mistake that for the captain's sake,
It's just as well that sighs is not important-oh.

What will your mother say, what will your mother say,
What will your mother say when she do know-ee-oh?
Her mother she did say, as under him she lay:
"Did you think that I was Pretty Penny-oh?"

Come tripping down the stair, come tripping down the stair,
Come tripping down the stairs all misbegotten-oh;
He came tripping down the stairs, because she's left her hairbrush there,
And he ended in a heap all at the bottom-oh.

But when I went ho, when I went ho,
When I went home from Limpenhoe,
The captain was the lover of Penny and her mother,
And they often performed all in a trio-ee-oh.

SID KIPPER SAYS: *"A lot of people don't know where Limpenhoe is. Well, that's nothing. A lot of people in Limpenhoe don't know what day it is. Which is daft, because it's definitely Tuesday."*

85

THE TWENTY POUND FROG

Now all on the feast of St Vit - as I put on me best hat and coat; I ent - ered me frog for the rac - ing, And he went to the front from the go. Oh Dand - y, he was a champ - ion; Mick Mack - erel's a dirt - y old dog. He came down the road With his Nat - ter - jack toad, And murd - ered me twen - ty pound frog.

SID KIPPER SAYS: *"The frog racing used to be held at Hardley Fair. A lot of people preferred it to horse-racing because anyone could train up a frog and enter, whereas racehorses are more difficult, and you can't get them in your pocket. Or, if you can, you can't keep your trousers up."*

But I digress. All the time. It helps make the days go by.

Since I've been here there's been a number of births, marriages, and deaths. Though not necessarily in that order. I suppose the biggest was mother. Well, you can't get bigger than the big sleep. That's what Christopher Marlowe called it. She went in 1996. At the age of 102. Not bad for an old 'un! I wasn't at her bedside. But it wouldn't have made any difference if I had been. She died in a fracas at the Women's Bright Hour. Something to do with a best decorated-matchbox competition. It's what she would have wanted.

Kenneth got married in 1997. To a girl I've never met. Hazel. Apparently she's very nice. And has all her own teeth. That's better than he deserves, if you ask me. Kevin enjoys the bachelor life. He was born in 1972. I forget if I remembered to mention it.

Kenneth and Hazel gave me a great-grandson in 1999. Kerry Kipper. They say he takes after his grandfather. Poor little mite.

Annie and Sid show no signs. I was a bit worried that while the cat was away the mice might play. I needn't have. Sid's more likely to run after the farmer's wife. And Annie's just a wee, sleekit, cow'rin', tim'rous beastie. To coin a phrase.

We don't hear a lot from Karen. That's not surprising. Not much news gets out of East Raynham.

Oh, and in the year 2000 Henry passed away. It was in the Trunch Trumpet. They asked if I wanted to go to the funeral. So I did. Well, not to the actual funeral. I spent the afternoon in the Old Goat Inn. It seemed a shame to waste the opportunity. I'm sure Henry wouldn't have understood.

Now all on the feast of St Vitas
I put on me best hat and coat;
I entered me frog for the racing,
And he went to the front from the go.

Though the rest of the field tried to catch him
My Dandy kept one jump ahead;
He'd have led by a neck if he'd had one,
And straight for the finish he sped.

> Oh Dandy, he was a champion;
> Mick Mackerel's a dirty old dog.
> He came down the road
> With his Natterjack toad,
> And murdered me twenty pound frog.

Well Dandy was surely the favourite,
He looked like he'd win it with ease,
But just then he jumped on a toadstool,
And the toad didn't seem at all pleased.

Now what happened next wasn't cricket;
It wasn't a lark nor a joke.
Mick Mackerel's toad had a frog in its throat,
And Dandy had croaked his last croak.

Chorus

I called for a stewards' enquiry;
I told them me Dandy was dead.
They said in that case he must lose second place,
Though he'd followed the toad by a head.

I wanted to wallop Mick Mackerel,
But he was a bit of a bruiser –
He was 6 foot 3 high, and the same again wide,
So I decided to be a good loser.

Chorus

Now all this had left me quite heated,
So I took off me coat and me hat,
And all the way home I felt naked,
For I'd nothing on under that.

Well I've learned me a twenty-pound lesson,
And I'll not forget it, don't fear.
I'll get me own back on Mick Mackerel –
I'm getting an adder next year!

Chorus

THE END OF AN ERROR Henry Kipper – 1914–2000
(from the *Trunch Trumpet*, 31/7/2000)

Henry 'Croaker' Kipper, father of folk mego-star Sid Kipper and erstwhile member of the Kipper Family, departed this earth on July 29th. After a long and painful existence, not least for his family, he passed away peacefully in mid anecdote. So, in a very real sense, he went quietly in everyone else's sleep.

Older son of William and Sarah, he was born on the day World War I broke out. His father noted in his diary at the time "This is the end of civilisation as we know it." Strangely, though, he made no mention of the War.

Henry grew up in St Just-near-Trunch, and did whatever work came his way that he couldn't avoid. In the 1980s, however, along with his talented son Sid, he was discovered by the folk scene, and for a few years they had a sensational career touring the country, recording albums, and appearing on TV and radio.

For the past few years Henry's whereabouts have been a complete mystery. He ran away from the Old Folkies Home to which he had been retired, and the family lost touch with him. Then, just two weeks before his death, he turned up out of the blue at the family cottage, and despite the change of locks managed to gain entrance. There they found him, sitting in his old chair by the fire, as if nothing had happened.

The service, conducted by the vicar of St Just, Revd 'Call-Me-Derek' Bream, was a colourful affair. Derek performed a rather modern form of funeral, which included the coffin being placed in the cloakroom according to the laws of *feng shui,* and the congregation standing and clapping their hands over their heads as they movingly sang 'Another One Bites The Dust'.

Henry leaves a widow, Dot, a son, Sid, and a brother, George.

THE FLAT OF THE LAND

There's peo-ple who just won't be told, I'm tel-ling you, it's true, Who rec-kon they know ev-ry-thing, and swear it till they're blue. Well, such a one came in the pub, just the o-ther week, Full of in-for-mat-ion, and not what you'd call meek. When asked for his op-in-ion on my coun-ty he just sneered; "Ve-ry flat, Nor-folk", but per-haps he meant the beer.

There's people who just won't be told, I'm telling you, it's true,
Who reckon they know everything, and swear it till they're blue.
Well such a one came in the pub, just the other week,
Full of information, and not what you'd call meek.
When asked for his opinion on my county he just sneered;
"Very flat, Norfolk", but perhaps he meant the beer.

I asked him if he'd been to Roman Camp, where eagles fly,
Or to the west of Weybourne, where you can see as far as Cley.
But though I painted pictures of long and lofty views,
He said he'd read it in a book, and so it must be true.
Just then my girlfriend came in, buttons straining on her vest,
He said "Very flat, Norfolk", as he ogled at her chest.

Now some delight in tolerance, at least that's what I've heard,
But I'm a man whose actions speak far louder than his words.
So to show him that the pen is not as mighty as the sword.
I took him down to Wroxham, and I dipped him in the Broad.
The final thing he told me, with his upper lip still stiff;
Was "Very flat, Norfolk", as he flew off Cromer Cliff.

So if you come to Norfolk – and you're welcome as can be –
Don't tell us what you've read somewhere, but go by what you see.
We've got high bits, low bits, and though it's not as I would wish,
Some parts that if I really must admit it are flattish.
But here's a tip if, in the pub, they ask you what you think,
Don't say "Very flat, Norfolk", say "It's fine – who'd like a drink?".

SID KIPPER SAYS: *"People who think Norfolk is flat should go to Lincolnshire. Or anywhere else, come to that."*

When you live somewhere you don't think about it. It's just normal. But not when you're away from there. Then you realise what you're missing. I suppose I'll even miss this place. When I go. If I go.

Some people say that Norfolk is awfully flat. That's because they're thinking of the Fens. Or possibly the Broads. If they're thinking at all. But that's only a little bit of Norfolk. The wet bit. That bit will all be washed away soon, anyway. Come global warming. Anyhow what's so awful about being flat? You wouldn't want lumpy pancakes, would you? You wouldn't want to live in a Council uneven. Well. I wouldn't.

They reckon that Yorkshire is God's own county. In that case Norfolk is where he takes his holidays. And Suffolk is where he goes when he's not feeling well and needs a long lie down. As for London, well. If he's half as clever as they make out he stays out of London altogether. People in London suffer from repetitive brain injury. Commonly known as political correctness gone mad. Where else would swede-bashing be called racist? Where else would you see a musical like 'Don't Call Me Madam'? Where else would you want to? Still, that's none of my business. If they like it there that's up to them. He who pays the piper picks a peck of pickled peppers. That's what I say. Well I would. If I could.

In about 1999 I got a letter. I read the envelope before I opened it. Written on it was 'FOND'. I thought perhaps it was like one of those wartime codes people used. Like SWALK. That was "sealed with a loving kiss". That was one of the more repeatable ones. So was HORWICH. That was "hat off ready when I come home". Writing NORWICH on the envelope was a lot ruder. Unless the person lived there. Of course. Well, it was supposed to be ruder, except you don't start knickers with an N. If you start them at all.

When I opened the letter it turned out FOND didn't stand for "Fling Off Nickers Dear" after all. It stood for Friends Of the Norfolk Dialect. They were just setting it up. They were contacting various Norfolk writers and artists. I was part of the variety. They wanted to know would I like to be a patron? Well. Far be it from me not to patronise someone when the opportunity presents. Sid had put me in for it. Naturally. He thought it would help take my mind off things.

It did exactly the opposite. It put my mind on things instead. I became homesick for Norfolk. I dreamed of Dersingham. I conjured up Catfield. I idealised Itteringham. When I started thinking fondly of Felbrigg I pulled myself up short. That was going too far. I had to stop this day-dreaming and do something. So I started writing songs. About Norfolk places. Some of them weren't half bad. If I say so myself. Like 'The Bluebells of Scottow'. Or 'Twenty-Four Hours From Tunstead'. 'New Buckenham! New Buckenham!' And 'The Loddon Derriere'. Well, that last one wasn't a song as such. More of rhapsody. In two parts.

I did join FOND. Everyone who's anyone did. Cyril Cockle didn't. Which just goes to prove my point. Lots of the members are old friends. And customers. Like that bloke from Radio Norfolk. Keith Skipper. I used to sell him hair restorer. That's always a good line, because it doesn't work. If it did it wouldn't be any good. Not to the seller. You'd sell one lot to a person and that would be that. But it doesn't work. So you can keep selling them more and more. It's a much better line than song-books. For instance. Sell someone one song-book and they'll never want another. No repeat trade.

THE WRITES OF MAN

Well now I'm going to write a song;
It's really very easy and it won't take long.
Take a simple beat with a simple tune,
And some simple ideas about the moon in June.

So now we get to the second verse,
You'll find it's really very much like the first.
By now you can see just how I do it,
And I think you must agree that there's nothing to it.

And now we come to the verse in the middle,
It could be livened up with some banjo or some fiddle.
But that's more than this song deserves,
And by now the tune should be getting on your nerves.

Now this verse is the one before last;
When you're enjoying yourself doesn't time fly fast?
I could have made a point about something or other,
But to tell the truth I simply can't be bothered.

And the climax is this very last stanza;
We're nearly at the end of the entire extravaganza;
So I hope you like this song I've penned,
For now we've finally reached the end;
Except that I'll repeat the line again;
And again, and again, and again, and again;
Until I drive you round the bend;
The End.

SID KIPPER SAYS: *"I wrote a song once. Well, I wrote it loads of times, actually, but it was still no good. Which just goes to prove there's more to song-writing than eyes the meat!"*

Song-writing is easy. People make too much fuss about it. I started one this morning. I'm calling it 'Open Prison Blues'. Well it's my song. So I can call it what I like. It starts:

Well I woke up this morning, jumped out of my bed *(oh yes, I did)*;

I woke up this morning, jumped out of my bed *(I should know – I was there)*;

Forgot I was in the top bunk, and landed on my head.

The bits in brackets are spoken. It saves on the music.

I got the open prison blues when I heard that cell door slam *(I assure you it's true)*;

I got the open prison blues when I heard that cell door slam *(well, it made me jump)*;

Oh the draught in here is dreadful, I must get a doorstop, as soon as I can.

You can see what I'm doing. Can't you? I'm saying that whoever you are, whatever your circumstances, there'll always be something to moan about. It's a comforting thought.

I'll knock out some more verses later. Mind you. People only really listen to the first verse. And the last. So I've already done the last one:

You know I'll go to sleep this evening, jump into my bed *(oh yes you do)*;

I'll go to sleep this evening, jump into my bed *(but not necessarily in that order)*;

I never would have had the open prison blues if I'd just kept out of the red *(assuredly)*.

Of course that's a modern song. I can do old traditional ones just as well. Here's one I've jotted down. 'The False Bridegroom':

The week after pancake day, as you'll hear if you hark,

We went to the park for to have us a lark,

But you don't find larks in the park after dark,

So we had to make our own amusement.

Notice how the words don't quite fit. That's very important for old songs. Gives the singer something to do.

Oh I loved this lass once, then I loved her twice,

And she said now I'd loved her we'd have to get spliced,

So now for my fun I must pay a high price,

For I've gone and I've promised to wed her.

I'll put in some stuff about watching her go off to church. Or something traditional like that. When I get a moment.

The parson who married us aloud he did cry;

All you that forbid it I'd have you draw nigh.

But the bastards kept quiet, so the noose it was tied,

For I'd gone and I'd promised to wed her.

I'm not sure about 'bastards'. It's not very traditional. Of course bastards are extremely traditional. It's just the word. Anyhow, in old songs you often have what they call a floating verse. A filler.

The men in yon forest asked questions profound,

Like how many of those would you get to the pound?

And I answered them back with such replies as I found,

Like what's it like having turnips for brains?

And then I'll round it off. With:

Oh dig me a grave, dig it short, wide and fat,

With roses around it, and lilies thereat;

I never guessed it would all come to that,

When I went and I promised to wed her.

Like I said. Song-writing is easy. I didn't say anything about quality.

BACKWATERSIDE

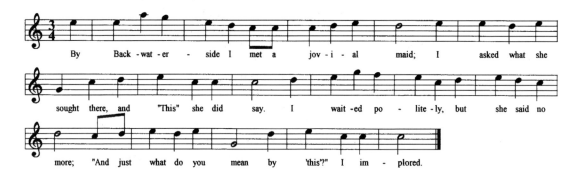

By Backwaterside I met a jovial maid;
I asked what she sought there, and "This," she did say.
I waited politely, but she said no more;
"And just what do you mean by 'this'?" I implored.

"Oh Sir, I said 'this', but I could have said 'that',
For I yearn for something, but I know not what."
"Then this something you yearn for, we must surely discover –
For if not this or that, then mayhap 'tis the other."

"Oh sir," she cried out, "you'll undo me I know;
It unhooks at the back and then slips off like so."
When I also was naked, she murmured, "My dear,
This thing that I yearn for, I have an idea."

It was clear from her words there was no need to coax;
So I tickled her fancy, and she soon got the joke.
When she'd finished laughing I was still poking fun,
So she polished her nails and said, "Let me know when you've done."

And as we two parted this maid said, "I've learned,
That having my leg pulled was not what I yearned.
But, Sir, you have helped me, for it came in a flash,
The thing I desire so is sausage and mash."

Well when nine months was over – 'twas surely no riddle –
This jovial young girl, she grew thick round the middle.
She grew big round the bottom, and tight round the top;
For eating sausage and mash, oh she just couldn't stop.

So come all you young men that go marching in May,
Though you think you're witty, the maids may nay-say.
And though you feel sure that your jest is a winner,
It may well turn out that she'd prefer a hot dinner.

SID KIPPER SAYS: *"Backwaterside is a spot round our way where courting couples have gone for generations. They still do, and I should know because I was up there only last week with my binoculars. That Tracey – she's a bit of a goer, I can tell you. Mind you, she's got plenty to go on."*

I don't miss women as much as I used to. The old juices have dried up. A bit. The urges have eased. Just as well, really.

The warden says that's normal. Says it happens to a lot of inmates. It's just human nature not to want what you can't have. You'd think he'd never been in the Old Goat Inn! You go in there. I promise you'll be wanting a decent pint soon enough.

Anyhow, I've got my memories. Not of a decent pint in the Old Goat. Of women. I only have to close my eyes and I can take my choice. In Technicolor. With surround sound.

I learned a lot when I'd just turned fourteen. From a handsome older woman. Blossom Bosom. I learned a lot from her. I learned that the world is full of lonely women. I learned that if a young man plays his cards right he might very well get an interesting invitation out of the blue. Unfortunately I also learned that if he was invited round for tea and cakes then tea and cakes might be all he got. Still, the lesson was free. And they were very nice cakes. Although at the time I wished there were less chocolate eclairs and cream horns. And more rock cakes.

A couple of months later I had another sort of lesson. In anatomy. I was taken upstairs by one of the girls at the Great Hall. I'd called there to deliver something. I forget what. And what does it matter to you now? "Gwennie" they called her. She said it was short for Gwen. Well, it wasn't her brains I was interested in. She said she had something to show me. She did too! That afternoon changed me, I can tell you. When I went upstairs with her I was just a boy. But when I came down again I was something more. I was an extremely happy boy. With a big smirk. After that I never looked back. I took to it like a fish to water. Like a fly to fishing. Like raspberries to jam.

Of course I was always discrete. Women appreciate that. They don't want everyone to know they're that sort of girl. Even if they are. Which makes it harder for men. Because they don't know if they're wasting their efforts or not. But I found that a woman can usually find a way of letting you know. Perhaps just a certain sort of smile. A wink. A twinkle in the eye. That sort of thing. Others are less subtle. Elsie Elver just sent me a pair of her unmentionables. With a note. Saying: "Come round and put these back on me. Afterwards." As Sid always says it's different strokes for different folks. It's just a matter of finding the bits that need stroking.

Sex is a great leveller. Unless you do it standing up. When it comes to the clinch we're all naked under our clothes. We're all the same height lying down. We are all, as old "Call-me" Derek says, but flesh. I find that very true. I certainly butted a fair bit of flesh in my youth.

I don't suppose Ruby has been faithful while I've been inside. She wasn't when I was out. She has needs. And I'm alright about that. It's only fair. Give and take. Box and cox. I can't complain. Mind you, if I find out who it is I'll shoot the swine.

I've often wondered about how some women aren't interested in that sort of thing. Like Annie. You don't get it with men. Nor does she, come to that. Oh, some men might be interested in different things to other men. Or they may just be interested in other men. Fair enough. But not many men aren't interested in anything of that sort. But some women really aren't. They'd rather do embroidery. Or go horse riding. Or be Prime Minister. It doesn't seem natural.

It's hard work. All this thinking and writing. I reckon I'll have to lie down and close my eyes for a bit. With Technicolor. And surround sound.

THIS IS MY LAND

This land is my land, my family got it,
By cheating, lying and fighting for it;
Then we enclosed it, the hedges grew stout,
To keep our stock in, and the likes of you out.
    This land is my land, and you'll regret it,
    If for one moment you should forget it.
    From that big oak tree, to the parish boundary,
    This land belongs to me alone.

This land is my land, if you want employment
You'll tug your forelock for my enjoyment.
You'll speak politely, and call me mister,
And let me sleep with your younger sister.

This land is my land, each path and trackway,
But if you walk them you'll have a black day.
You claim your right, if you think you've got one,
I know what I've got – a twelve-bore shotgun.

This land is my land, though you must mind it,
I set the rent here, and you must find it.
Don't give me tales of your empty larders,
If times are hard, well, they're getting harder.

This land is my land, though times are rotten,
With prices falling to rocky bottom.
So now your taxes pay my land's profit;
Well, thank you kindly – now bugger off it.

I'm going to travel when I get out of here. Sid's been all over. Cornwall. Devon. Dorset. He says they're all very nice. If you like that sort of thing. Which he does. I dare say I could do the odd deal. In clotted cream. Cheese. Things like that. You don't get them in Norfolk. That's due to farming being unmixed nowadays. When I was a boy you got all sorts of farming. There'd be cattle. And sheep. Pigs. Spuds. All sorts. Now it's just barley, sugarbeet, and rape. That last one is a funny name for a crop. It makes you wonder how they decided to grow it. "What'll you be sowing next year?" "Well, as a matter of fact I'm contemplating rape!"

When I think about it there's been huge changes. Well. Take our cowshed. It's had to be set aside now. Due to us having no cows. As I say, they went out of fashion. Mind you, I still made a few bob out of the shed.

It started when they turned the Goat Inn into the New Goat Inn. Back in 1904. Well my Uncle Albert took a fancy to the fixtures and fittings. So he let Old Ernie dump them at the back of our place. For a fiver. Albert got the fiver. Old Ernie went off happy enough. By all accounts. And Albert set the stuff up in the cowshed. It looked really smart, they reckon. He even made the beer pumps into a sort of a milking machine. It must have been the only milking parlour where the cows had a choice between a public bar and a lounge.

It all fell into disrepute when the cows left home. Until 1979. That's when they decided to do up the pub again. And call it the Old Goat. Well I had a chat with Young Ernie. I said I might be able to get my hands on some good old stuff. Authentic. And he bought the lot. At top dollar. I threw in the fitting for free. Well, I knew it would fit. Didn't I? It was much the same when I got the job of re-leading the church roof. Anyhow, Ernie was impressed. He said he'd never seen made-to-measure fittings before. I got free drinks for a month on top. And I didn't have to nick any of them. And the Old Goat changed back to exactly how it was before it changed into the New Goat. Except for the odd hoof mark on the benches. And the rusty hay racks on the walls. Ernie liked those. Said they made a nice change.

There's been so many changes during my life. Some of them because of me. Mostly not.

There's been the rise of the motor car, and the decline of the horse. Our horse declined so much he's dead.

There's been long skirts, short skirts, and all points in between.

Everyone I know has got older. Except policemen. They've got younger. I take that personally.

Folk-songs have come in and out of fashion like turn-ups.

Suffragettes have become feminists. Mind you, what's in a name? Most of them are still just women. As far as I can see. And I've looked closely.

Most things have gone metric. Either that or been decimalised.

North sea gas has come. They dug up half of Norfolk for that. Which wouldn't be so bad. If it weren't for the fact that most people in Norfolk can't get it.

Young women have got prettier. And young men have got stupider.

Summers have got shorter. And inclines have got longer.

The New Goat has become the Old Goat. I hear there's talk of it becoming Ye Olde Goatee. No doubt everyone will still call it The Goat.

Food has got faster, and I've become slower.

The hula-hoop has come and gone.

Cyril Cockle has got even more objectionable.

People in glass houses still throw stones.

And on the whole everything has turned out for the best.

It makes you wonder what the future holds.

SID KIPPER SAYS: *"Years ago a lot of land was common. Hence the saying 'common is muck'. Then they had what they called the foreclosures, and the land wasn't common any more. But all the people who'd been thrown off it were!"*

HATE STORY

I hate my bro-ther, I hate him like no o-ther, For years and years and years I've held that view; And I don't mind bet-ting, that if you ev-er met him, Then you'd hate my bro-ther too.

I'll tell you what the future holds for me. A lot more of the same. Because they reckon I can't have parole. They say it's because I won't admit my guilt. So I haven't reformed. There's the eye-rub. So I'll have to do the full stretch. I can't simply admit my guilt, because I didn't do it. Not that I mind lying. You understand. But I know their tricks. If I say I did it after all they'll have me up for perjury. I've been around too long to fall for that one.

Sid says he's going to have a campaign. Free The Trunch One! He says he knows some important people. But I'm not holding my breath. He won't say who they are.

Sid's done very well for himself. He's done tours. And albums. And books. He's even got a logo. I reckon I'll have one of those when I get out. I've worked out the design. It'll be simple. And dignified. Just the initials GK, in capital letters, in an oval. Coloured green. You can probably visualise it.

I asked Sid about our double act. He just said what double act? I said I'd sort of thought he was just hanging on for me to come out and join him. He said not on your nelly. He said he'd learned a lot since Henry retired. Being solo meant you made all the decisions. And didn't have to split the fee. I hadn't realised people actually paid him.

So I reckon I'll go solo too. When I get out. I should have a bit of a start. Due to some of my songs being so well known. I suppose I've got Sid to thank for that. But I'm not the grateful sort, so he can whistle for it.

Now there's a thought. I'll do an album, and get Sid to perform on it. Only I'll just let him whistle in the background. That'll pay him back for all those backing vocals. I may not be the grateful sort, but I do know how to nurse a grudge.

The warden says that nowadays they can do these tests. DNA. To tell you who someone's parents are. Who's whose. So to speak. Perhaps I should have them done for me and Sid. Then I'd know for sure. Then again I don't see how I'd be any better off than just assuming. And I'd be worse off if it came out the other way. So best let lying dogs sleep. I suppose.

Would I have changed anything in my life? Loads of things. You think I volunteered to stay where I've been for nearly twenty years? With nothing to do but run the library. And write this.

Although now I've finished I feel quite good about it. If I dropped dead tomorrow at least there'd be this book for people to remember me by. Then again. Given my luck it'll probably be just another target for page benders. I hate them.

Still, it's too late to change anything now. In the book. Or in my life. So there it was, then. That was my life. Take it or leave it. I had to.

I hate my brother, I hate him like no other,
For years and years and years I've held that view;
And I don't mind betting, that if you ever met him,
Then you'd hate my brother too.

I hate the neighbours, my malice never wavers,
And my brother always says he shares my view;
And I know that it's true, if you lived where we do,
Then you'd hate the neighbours too.

I hate Knapton, where terrible things happen,
And I know that the neighbours share my view;
And if you lived in Trunch, where we're such a friendly bunch,
Then you'd hate Knapton too.

I hate Norwich, they're all as pale as porridge.
And I know my mates in Knapton share my view;
And if you'd ever been there, and seen the sordid scene there,
Then you'd hate Norwich too.

I hate Suffolk, they're a real pain in the buttocks,
And I know the whole of Norfolk shares my view;
If you saw the disorder, that occurs over the border,
Then you'd hate Suffolk too.

I hate London, they're hard as carborundum,
And all of us provincials share that view;
And if you'd ever heard, the way they say their words,
Then you'd hate London too.

I hate the French, with loathing so intense,
And everyone in England shares my view;
And if you went abroad, you'd see nothing to applaud,
And you would hate the French too.

I hate Yanks, the lot of them are cranks,
And all us Europeans share that view;
And if you ever should, eat what they describe as food,
Then you would hate Yanks too.

I hate you, you're not like me,
But I think I see a way that this could end;
The world will live as one, when the Aliens come,
Then we'll all be united hating them.

INDEX OF SONGS

1 – copyright Dick Nudds/Chris Sugden.
2 – copyright Chris Sugden.

All or part of the songs in this book may be heard on the following albums:

FY – *Fresh Yesterday*, by the Kipper Family. Dambuster Records, DAM020
ATMG – *Arrest These Merry Gentlemen*, by the Kipper Family. Dambuster Records, DAM022
ITFW – *In The Family Way*, by the Kipper Family. Dambuster Records, DAM023
LARP – *Like A Rhinestone Ploughboy*, by Sid Kipper. Leader Records, LER2115
BITB – *Boiled In The Bag*, by Sid Kipper. Leader Records, LER2118
ESS – *East Side Story*, by Sid Kipper. Leader Records, LER2120
CM – *Chained Melody*, by Sid Kipper. Leader Records, LER2122

Acknowledgements: The business cards featured on page 1 appear courtesy of A. Kipper (Miss), of the Coote Memorial Museum at St Just-near-Trunch. An exhaustive collection of cards may be seen at the Museum. Then again, it may not.

Also available from Mousehold Press, by the same authors:

PREWD AND PREJUDICE (1994)
When Miriam Prewd left polite London society for the depths of rural Norfolk, she was shocked at what she found. The year was 1904, but St Just-near-Trunch was only half-civilised. Plants grew unchecked, unruly birds woke her before dawn, there was not a milliner for miles and Harrods flatly refused to deliver. From then on it could only get worse.

THE BALLAD OF SID KIPPER (1996)
The cream of Sid Kipper's early repertoire, featuring the words and music of 36 of Sid's songs with commentaries by the man himself. Add a thirteen-page biography, photographs, four stories, a play, a dance, a walnut-shell workshop and instructions for the singing of folk-songs, and you have a veritable cornucopia of resources. With the emphasis on the corn.

CRAB WARS (1999)
It was personal: for Cromeo and Sheriet, two young lovers parted by hatred; for Elsie Primrose, who was no better than she ought to be; for Blake Vincent, thrust into the job of Town Crier just as his voice was breaking; for Doctor Flawd, a man who never let the symptoms get in the way of a good diagnosis; and for the Market Forces, a gang of persuasive young men who demanded much and supplied little. All these, and many more, were caught up in a turmoil of events which seemed as if it would never be resolved. But it was.

COD PIECES (2001)
Dozens of stories, poems and recipes. Specially selected morsels of prime Kipper, lovingly hand-shaped and rippled through with a hint of sage. Ideal as a substantial main course, or dip in for a tasty snack. Keep cool and dry after opening.

To find out more about Sid Kipper and his relatives, join his mailing list at:
10 Perseverance Road, Queensbury, Bradford, BD13 1LY. Or visit www.sidkipper.co.uk